Numerical BASIC

by

Bruce Douglass

Howard W. Sams & Co., Inc.
4300 WEST 62ND ST. INDIANAPOLIS, INDIANA 46268 USA

International Standard Book Number: 0-672-22048-2
Library of Congress Catalog Card Number: 83-50711

Edited by: *J. L. Davis*
Illustrated by: *Kevin Caddell*

Printed in the United States of America.

PREFACE

With the advent of the personal computer, there is a great need for information about their use. No longer are the main computing facilities in the hands of expertly trained computer scientists. Now, people from many fields are using personal computers for many different purposes. Since these people using the personal computers are not, as a group, expertly trained, there is a large "information gap" that must be bridged if the personal computers are to be used constructively. One of the areas of this information gap is the area of computational ("numerical") mathematics. Formerly, programs requiring sophisticated mathematics could be written using library routines already available on the main-frame computers. Since these are rare for microcomputers, it is necessary for microcomputer users to become acquainted with the methods and techniques of numerical mathematics and how to implement them on microcomputers.

Primarily, these people are neither computer scientists nor mathematicians, so the standard theoretical approach to numerical mathematics, appropriate in the university setting, is inappropriate for these users. It is this audience to which *Numerical BASIC* is addressed. Theory is kept to an absolute minimum and intuitive understanding is stressed. It is hoped that readers will finish the book with a gut understanding, an intuitive "feel" for the physical interpretations of these techniques and methods of implementation so that the numerical methods can be put to immediate use in their application programs.

This book makes certain assumptions about the mathematical expertise of its readership. One year of college mathematics (or equivalent) is mandatory, but a year of calculus would be very helpful. For some sections it is assumed that the reader is at least remotely familiar with matrices. Further readings are available in the references for those readers wishing to pursue a topic in more depth. The book also assumes that the reader is familiar enough with the BASIC programming language to follow the program examples.

The programs were written to run on the TRS-80 microcomputer with Disk BASIC, but any computer running Microsoft BASIC with 16K of available memory should be able to run the programs with little or no modification. For other computers, such as the Apple and Atari, Appendix A has been included to aid in translating the programs. The most important thing to get from this book is not the program listings, but the methods of numerical mathematics. If this goal is achieved, the reader can write any of these programs for any computer, in any language, and for virtually any application.

With me, as with all people, my philosophy is implicit in my writings. It's based on the idea that objective knowledge is possible and man can achieve it through rational means. This goes against the grain of many university professors these days who would try to refute the Aristotelian notions that "A is A" and "A thing is either A or not A" (the Law of Identity and the Law of the Excluded Middle). Even in the physical sciences, one hears the obvious attempts to refute these laws, and the state of the social sciences is even worse. Implicit in this book is the idea that numerical methods are a tool for the acquisition of objective knowledge about physical phenomena. This philosophy is called *Objectivism* and is more thoroughly explored in the writings of Ayn Rand and Leonard Peikoff.

I hope that the readers of this book find it enjoyable and the numerical methods discussed to be useful in their work. Readers interested in commercially available software in this genre may wish to contact my company, A-Priori Software, 1005 West Main, Vermillion, SD 57069. This software includes inexpensive diskettes containing the programs presented in this book, should you wish to avoid typing in all the program listings. Diskettes and tapes are available for many popular microcomputers. Check with A-Priori Software for availability of these programs for your particular computer.

BRUCE DOUGLASS

ACKNOWLEDGMENTS

I wish to acknowledge the invaluable aid of my friend and comrade Dorkdork the Magnificent (known to mortals as Doris Minnerath) for proofreading the manuscripts, and the assistance of the editors at The Blacksburg Group, particularly Jon Titus, for their many useful comments and suggestions. This book was prepared on a TRS-80 Model I with Newscript 7.0, an excellent word-processing program from PROSOFT, Box 560, North Hollywood, CA 91603.

This book is dedicated to Howard Roark.

CONTENTS

CHAPTER 1

Error analysis and the Microcomputer—Number systems—Floating-Point Representation—Sources and Types of Numerical Error—Absolute and Relative Errors—Avoiding Numerical Errors

CHAPTER 2

Basic Differential Calculus—Basic Integral Calculus— Fundamental Theorem of Calculus—Rectangle Method of Numerical Integration—Trapezoid Rule for Integration

CHAPTER 3

Bisection Method—Newton-Raphson Iteration—Horner's Algorithm—Solving for All Roots—System of Nonlinear Equations—Note on Partial Derivatives

CHAPTER 4

Matrix Arithmetic—Gaussian Elimination and the Sweep Operator—Systems of Linear Equations—Scaled Partial Pivoting—Word Problems—Iterative Matrix Methods— Using SEIDEL

APPENDIX B

APPENDIX C

CHAPTER 1

INTRODUCTION TO NUMERICAL METHODS

Numerical methods is a branch of mathematics that concerns the computational aspects of physical problems rather than the theoretical aspects. This branch of mathematics is covered in many books and several professional journals are devoted to it. However, much of this information is unavailable to the layperson computerist for a variety of reasons.

Some of the methods require a sophisticated mathematical background to understand their derivations. Most books on numerical methods, even the introductory texts, place a great emphasis on understanding the derivations of the computational algorithms. The importance of this cannot be denied—often algorithms are accurate within specific ranges only when certain conditions are met. Taylor series approximations (widely used methods of approximating functions such as tan x and ln x, are often only applicable as long as you stay within a specific range of values. The Taylor series for tan x, for example, is only valid as long as x is between $-\pi/2$ and $\pi/2$. For values outside this range, x must be reduced somehow to a value within this range in order to get the correct answer. You must ascertain these conditions and make sure that they are satisfied, and you must determine how to handle the problem when these conditions are not met. The behavior of the function under conditions for which it is not meant to operate is called its "robustness" of the method. This level of understanding can only come about by means of a thorough understanding of the derivations of the individual numerical methods. *However, a detailed knowledge is not necessary for many users of numerical methods.* Many, perhaps even most, users of numerical methods need not greatly concern themselves with the theoretical aspects of numerical methods. They wish only to use the methods and need only an intuitive understanding of the methods and their limitations in order to use them. In other words, they only want the answers. This may apply to scientists, students, engineers, and others who have many constraints on their time and who need to compute answers to questions.

This book fills the gap between theoretical numerical methods and the uninitiated end user of these methods. A smattering of theory will be introduced, but intuitive understanding will be stressed. The algorithms will be given with explanations, computer subroutines, and programs, as well as example problems. The subroutines will be presented in BASIC, the most universal computer language, and they will be written specifically to run on the TRS-80 microcomputer using Disk BASIC, except where noted. Since this microcomputer uses a widely popular version of Microsoft BASIC, users of other computers should have little difficulty in translating the routines for their own systems.

Before we introduce any numerical methods per se, it behooves us to become acquainted with the way in which the computer, particularly the microcomputer, uses numbers and how errors in our answers can (and will) come up. This very important section of numerical methods is called . . .

ERROR ANALYSIS AND THE MICROCOMPUTER

Before we can begin looking at just where errors come from in computer mathematics, we must understand how numbers are stored and manipulated by the computer. The errors that arise from a computer's manipulation of numbers are dependent on the storage method used.

There are three primary modes for storing numbers in computers: *integer, single-precision,* and *double-precision.* Some languages, such as Pascal, define other numerical types, such as "large integers" and Boolean types, but we will concern ourselves only with these three primary types.

NUMBER SYSTEMS

For several thousand years, we have used a "place" number system. That means simply that the position of a digit in a number is important in determining its value. Take the number 312. The 3 is in the hundred's place, meaning that we take 100 times 3 to get the value of that digit; the 1 is in the ten's place, giving us 1×10 and the 2 is in the one's place, giving us 2×1. The value for the whole number is merely the sum of the digits in their places, e.g., $312 = 3 \times 100 + 1 \times 10 + 2 \times 1$. Is a pattern beginning to emerge?

The "place values" represent powers of 10. The hundred's place is 10^2, the ten's place is 10^1, and the one's place is 10^0. In this number system, called the *decimal system*, the base is 10, and successive powers of the base are used to determine the place value for each digit. The same is true for other number systems. The most important number systems are binary, octal, decimal, and hexadecimal, which use bases of 2, 8, 10, and 16, respectively. In general, a string of decimal digits represents a number according to the following formula:

$$A_n A_{n-1} \ldots A_2 A_1 A_0 = A_n \times 10^n + A_{n-1} \times 10^{n-1} + \ldots + A_0 \times 10^0$$

This takes care of the whole numbers, but what about fractions? The same general principle holds, except now the digits are divided by successive powers of the base. In general, then, we have

$$0.B_1 B_2 B_3 \ldots = B_1 \times 10^{-1} + B_2 \times 10^{-2} + B_3 \times 10^{-3} + \ldots$$

Putting these two types of numbers together, we can state that, in general, all numbers can be represented in the following format:

$$
\begin{aligned}
A_n A_{n-1} \ldots A_1 A_0 . B_1 B_2 \ldots &= A_n \times 10^n + A_{n-1} 10^{n-1} + \ldots + A_0 \times 10^0 \\
&\quad + B_1 \times 10^{-1} + B_2 \times 10^{-2} + \ldots \\
&= \sum_{k=0}^{k=n} A_K \beta^k + \sum_{k=1}^{k=\infty} B_k \beta^{-k}
\end{aligned}
\tag{1-1}
$$

where β is the base of the number system.

Now the same is true, as suggested by Equation 1-1, of all number bases. Computers don't work in base 10; they work in base 2. Base 2 is just like base 10 (if you're missing most of your fingers!). Counting in base 2 is simple. Table 1-1 shows binary/decimal equivalents.

You will notice that each position in a binary number is a power of 2. Thus 100 base 2 equals 4 base 10, because 4 is 2 to the second power, and so on.

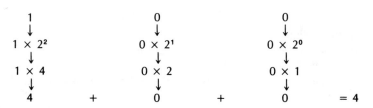

Table 1-1. Binary/Decimal Equivalents

Binary	Decimal
0	0
1	1
10	2
11	3
100	4
101	5
110	6
111	7
1000	8
1001	9
1010	10
1011	11
1100	12
1101	13
1110	14
1111	15
10000	16

FLOATING-POINT REPRESENTATION

A detailed understanding of the different numbering systems isn't that important for what we are considering here but it is necessary to understand *floating-point representation* of numbers, and why this causes errors in number representation.

In decimal floating-point representation, all numbers can be represented as decimal fractions. For example, the number 13,592 is the same as 0.13592 × 100,000, or 0.13592 × 10^5. The general representation is

$$\pm 0.A_1 A_2 A_3 \ldots \times 10^n$$

where A_1 is nonzero and n is an integer. The *mantissa* is the number without the exponent term. Notice that the representations 1.2342 × 10^8 and 0.00231 × 10^3 are not in this form, because the first significant (nonzero) digit does not immediately follow the decimal point. In binary, the representation would be, of course,

$$\pm 0.A_1 A_2 A_3 \ldots \times 2^n$$

Note that "digit" A_1 is nonzero. If it is ever zero, then the digits can be moved to the left and the exponent incremented. This is called *normalization* of the number. The basic difference between single- and double-precision numbers is the number of bytes provided for storing the mantissa. On the TRS-80 microcomputer, for example, single-precision numbers use 4 bytes of storage and double-precision numbers use 8 bytes. Both use one byte for storing the exponent term, but single-precision uses 3 bytes for the mantissa while double-precision uses 7.

SOURCES AND TYPES OF NUMERICAL ERROR

To demonstrate the source of errors in numerical computations, consider a "picocomputer" system that uses only 3 bits for a floating-point number. That is, the representation is

$$0.A_1 A_2 A_3 \times 2^n$$

The As can be either 0 or 1, and the exponent, n, can be -1, 0, or $+1$ (for now, let's assume our numbers are positive). You will notice that the smallest number that can be represented is 0.001×2^{-1}, if we relax the constraint about all numbers being normalized. This is equal to 1/16 in decimal. Any number smaller than this but larger than zero would result in a 0 being used as the representative number. *This kind of error is called underflow.* On the other hand, the largest number is $0.111 \times 2^{+1}$, which is equal to 7/4. *Any number larger than this would cause an overflow error,* meaning that the number is too large to be represented in this computer. In all, only 24 numbers can be represented by this particular number system. These 24 numbers are the only ones that can be represented exactly in this format; all other numbers are mere approximations. The numbers that can be represented are called *machine numbers.*

The TRS-80 uses many more bits for storage, but nevertheless the same problem arises; only a finite set of numbers may be represented exactly, and all others will be approximated as one of the machine numbers. All the numbers could be represented if we used unlimited bits, but since we must truncate (i.e., cut off) the number of bits somewhere, this type of error is called *truncation error.*

ABSOLUTE AND RELATIVE ERRORS

If a given real number, x, falls between two machine numbers, A and B, then it will be represented as either A or B. The process of representing a real number by the closest machine number is called *rounding* and the error introduced by rounding is called *roundoff error.* Let's presume our machine rounds to the nearest machine number, A. The *absolute error* in the representation is $|A-x|$. In practice we don't know the absolute error, and we won't worry about it other than to note its existence. A more important measure of this error is *relative error*. It is given by $|(A-x)/x|$; this is the roundoff error we get when we represent the real number by a machine number, expressed as a percent.

Single-precision numbers are normally displayed as six digits. Let's do some arithmetic with these types of numbers and see what errors arise. For example, we'll use two floating-point decimal numbers, A = 0.123456×10^6 and B = 0.4567891×10^1. Adding A and B gives

```
    123456.000000
 +  000004.567891
    123460.567891, or 0.123460567891 × 10⁶
```

The computed sum would actually be represented as 0.123460×10^6 since those digits beyond the first six are truncated, or "cut off." This gives an absolute error of 0.567891 and a relative error of 4.59977×10^{-6}.

In this situation the error is not really too bad, but remember in repeated calculations it can accumulate enough to (possibly) make your final answer meaningless! A particularly severe type of error occurs when you subtract two numbers which have almost equal values. For example, let A = 0.991012312 and B = 0.991009987. Subtracting B from A gives

```
   0.991012312
 - 0.991009987
   0.000002325 = 0.2325 × 10⁻⁵
```

Truncating the numbers to only six digits of precision, the computer will come up with

```
   0.991012
 - 0.991010
   0.000002 = 0.2000 × 10⁻⁵
```

This gives us an absolute error of 0.325×10^{-6}, and a relative error of

$$\frac{(A-B)-[M(A)-M(B)]}{A-B}$$

where we've used $M(A)$ as the machine representation of A and $M(B)$ as the machine representation of B, that is, as the truncated numbers. This equals $0.000000325/0.000002325$, or 0.139785. Notice that we have a huge relative error—this means that our answer is off by a whopping 13 percent! Can you imagine what would happen in a computation that required repeated arithmetic manipulation?

The TRS-80 has slightly better precision than six digits, even though only six are displayed. Typically, most computers display garbage digits that are tagged on to the answer by the computer, even though they are meaningless. For example, the subtraction for this problem gave a result of 0.0000023458, which yields a relative error of $|(0.2325 - 0.23458)/0.2325| = 0.008946$, which can be multiplied again and again, propagating and accumulating numerical error.

AVOIDING NUMERICAL ERRORS

As a numerical analyst and computer programmer, you need to be aware of these sources of error. For example, if you use the equation, $x = 1 - \cos a$, in a program, you could be losing significant accuracy when the value of a is close to 0. You might recall from trigonometry that

$$1 - \cos a = 2 \sin\left(\frac{a}{2}\right)$$

The latter formulation will yield much better accuracy when the value for a is close to 0.

There are lots of examples where rewriting the function in a mathematically equivalent fashion will avoid serious roundoff errors. A truncated Maclaurin series can often be used. For example,

$$f(x) = \frac{e^x - 1}{x}$$

can be written as

$$f(x) = \frac{1}{x}\left(1 + x + \frac{x^2}{2} + \frac{x^3}{6} + R - 1\right)$$

$$= 1 + x/2 + x^2/3! + R/x$$

where

R = remaining terms in the expansion of e^x,

$n! = 1 \times 2 \times 3 \times 4 \times \ldots \times (n-1) \times n$.

We will discuss Maclaurin and Taylor series later, but *you can see how this will avoid serious roundoff error around $x = 0$.* On the other hand, if x is not close to 0, it will be more economical to use the original formula. A simple subroutine for the function evaluation would be as follows:

```
1000  REM X IS PARAMETER PASSED
1010  IF ABS(X)<.05 THEN F=(EXP(X)−1)X:GOTO 1100
1020  F=1+X/2+X↑2/6
1100  RETURN
```

Continuing with the use of series, let's say we use the first six terms of the above series. Is there an optimal way to evaluate the series so that we minimize the number of computations? This would have the effect of *speeding up the evaluation* as well as *minimizing error*. The series we are concerned with looks like this:

$$f(x) = 1 + \frac{x}{2} + \frac{x^2}{6} + \frac{x^3}{24} + \frac{x^4}{120} + \frac{x^5}{720}$$

Note that x is a factor for each term other than the first. We can factor out the $x/2$, leaving

$$f(x) = 1 + \frac{x}{2}\left(1 + \frac{x}{3} + \frac{x^2}{12} + \frac{x^3}{60} + \frac{x^4}{360}\right)$$

But note that the rightmost four terms inside the parentheses can have $x/3$ factored out, etc., etc. After the smoke clears, you are left with

$$f(x) = 1 + \frac{x}{2}\left(1 + \frac{x}{3}\left\{1 + \frac{x}{4}\left[1 + \frac{x}{5}\left(1 + \frac{x}{6}\right)\right]\right\}\right)$$

This formulation is called *Horner's algorithm,* and it will be discussed in greater detail later.

On the TRS-80, running at 1.77 MHz, exponentiation of two single-precision numbers requires about 50 milliseconds (ms); addition takes about 630 microseconds (μs); multiplication takes 2.2 ms, and division requires 4.8 ms. The first formulation of the series has four exponentiations, five divisions, and five additions, requiring a total time of approximately 227.15 ms. The last formulation has no exponentiations, five divisions, five multiplications, and five additions, totaling 38.15 ms—a speedup factor of 6. Further, most computer-based exponentiation routines use an optimized Taylor series with several terms, each with its own error. By minimizing the use of these routines, we maximize our accuracy as well.

Another example is given in Program 1-1. It is a simple program that merely sums up exp $(−x/6)$ for $x=0$ to $x=50$ and then sums the same function from $x=50$ down to $x=0$. You might like to run the program, and try to explain the results without reading further.

Program 1-1. Summing Up and Down

```
 10 FOR X=0 TO 50
 20   E = E + EXP(−X/6)
 30 NEXT I
 40 PRINT "SUM FORWARDS =" ;E
 50 E=0
 60 FOR X=50 TO 0 STEP −1
 70   E = E + EXP(−X/6)
 80 NEXT I
 90 PRINT "SUM BACKWARDS =";E
100 END
```

Now that you've run the program, you're probably wondering why the two sums are different. All we did was reverse the direction of the summation. That's the key! As we summed forwards the sum got larger, but the numbers we added got very small indeed. In fact, the relative error became huge because we lost so many digits by adding a large number to a very small one. Eventually, we had underflow errors during the addition because the sum was much, much greater than the number being added. On the other hand, what about the backwards summation? Here we started with the small numbers and they got larger as the sum got larger. Here, the relative error did not become huge, because we did not truncate so many digits when the number added was so small — it was being added to a another small number, so more digits were retained. As the sum got larger, so did the number being added, maintaining roughly equal roundoff error at each addition. Therefore, for the "backwards summation," from 50 down to 0 the sum will be larger and more accurate for this series. *You must look intelligently at what your programs are doing to even notice these simple ways of minimizing error.* Look at the function being evaluated. Is it being iterated (evaluated repeatedly)? Will the values being added get small as the sum of the iteration gets large? Are the valid ranges for the function being exceeded? Is there some part of the evaluation process especially prone to serious roundoff error, such as the subtraction of two numbers close to each other in value, and can you rewrite the function to avoid the error?

With appropriate foresight into the numbers that constitute an acceptable range for the numerical method used and into the range of values that the program will actually see (which may not be the same), it will be possible to design the algorithms to avoid these severe types of error. In some cases, you will use an IF-THEN command to test for the correct range of inputs and to make appropriate transformations to the input values (such as for periodic functions). You may use equivalent formulations that yield less error for the given input value. In any event, you should pay attention to the sources of numerical error and try to avoid them when designing programs around numerical algorithms.

CHAPTER 2

INTRODUCTION TO CALCULUS AND THE COMPUTER

Wait! Come back! Calculus is not difficult! You've been lied to!

It's true. The first thing you learn in school is that mathematics is "hard, but you've got to learn it anyway." This attitude on the part of teachers whom I have seen goes a long way toward the formation of mental blocks about learning mathematics. Math is just a language that concerns itself with quantities rather than qualities. It doesn't care about "what" as much as "how much." That doesn't mean that mathematics is trivial, or that parts of it are not difficult to understand. What I mean is that it is not difficult to gain at least an intuitive understanding about what mathematics does and how it does it.

I'm beginning the numerical methods with an introduction to calculus for a good reason; in this chapter we will develop an intuitive understanding of a number of concepts and numerical methods that will be used throughout this book. A more advanced treatment of calculus will be given later in the book, but, for now, an intuitive introduction is in order.

Algebra is a description of the world as it is. It views the world as a static, unchanging place, and provides tools to quantify what is going on in the world.

For example, if you have to pack 4096 books into boxes, and you can get boxes that will hold 128 books each, how many boxes will you need? Algebra supplies the method for finding the quantity. First, you set up the equation, with x standing for the unknown quantity of boxes:

$$x \times 128 = 4096$$

And by dividing both sides of the equation by 128, we obtain the value $x = 32$.

Calculus is analogous to algebra, in that it entails taking a certain perspective of the world. The perspective taken by calculus is that the world is changing, and calculus concerns itself quantifying the manner in which it changes. The leap from algebra to calculus is kind of like replacing a black-and-white television with a color set. A whole new world becomes available, but the world does become a little more complex.

Calculus is divided into two different parts. *Differential calculus* is specifically concerned with how things are changing at any instant in time. The quantitative measure of change is called a *differential* or a *derivative. Integral calculus* deals with changes over a period. In fact, differential and integral calculus are different sides to the same coin in the same sense that addition and subtraction are. We will deal with differential calculus first.

BASIC DIFFERENTIAL CALCULUS

Differential calculus deals with changes that are going on right now. Let's examine what "change" means geometrically. If you look at Fig. 2-1, you see a line. How fast are the y values changing on that line? If we denote the change in y by $\Delta y = y_1 - y_2$, and the change in x by $\Delta x = x_1 - x_2$, then the y values are changing at a rate of $\Delta y / \Delta x$. This is what is meant by the *slope* of the line. Notice that the line has a constant slope, that is, it rises at a constant rate. Therefore the derivative of the line (its slope) is constant. In this case, since $y_1 = 1$, $y_2 = 3$, $x_1 = 1$, and $x_2 = 4$, the slope is 2/3.

But most things are not straight lines but rather curves. Look at Fig. 2-2. It is a plot of $y = x^2$. Notice here that the slope is not constant, but rather is different at different points. The slope of such a curve at any point is defined to be the slope of the line tangent to the curve at that point. So, "What's a tangent?"

The concept of a tangent line can be thought of easily in terms of a limiting value for a secant line. Yes, I know—"What's a secant?" In Fig. 2-3, notice the various lines intersecting the curve at two points. These are called *secant lines.* Suppose we want to know the tangent to the curve at the point labeled G. We can use the line that goes through points A and B (which we will call line AB). But that's pretty far away isn't it? We could use the line CD. That's closer. But the line EF is closer still. Get the idea?

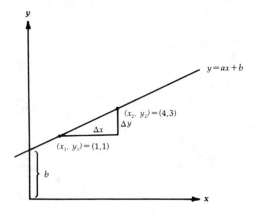

Fig. 2-1. A linear function.

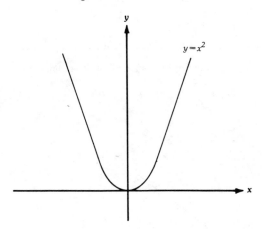

Fig. 2-2. A nonlinear function.

The tangent line is the *limit* of the secant lines as the points at which the secant line intersects the curve get closer to G. The slope of the tangent line is called the *derivative* of the curve at the point G. Note that the slope for a tangent line will be different for different points along the curve. The only "curve" for which this is not true is, of course, a straight line, which is its own tangent line.

An important concept was used here—that of a limit. This is one of the most important ideas that led to the development of calculus in the first place. Since we are still using Euclidean geometry (remember Mr. Barlett in high school helping you draw those congruent triangles?) we can always find a point between *any* two points. This

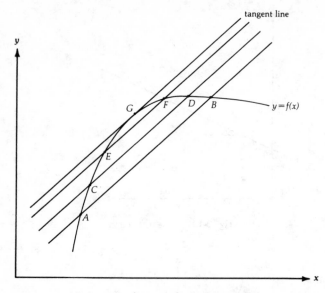

(A) A tangent line as a limit of secant lines.

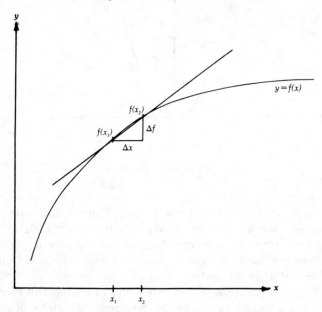

(B) Slope of secant connecting $(x_1, f(x_1))$ and $(x_2, f(x_2))$ is $(f(x_2) - f(x_1))/(x_2-x_1)$ $= \Delta f/\Delta x$.

Fig. 2-3. Finding the derivative at a point on a curve.

means that we can always get a "better" secant line approximation to the tangent line that we are using, no matter how close we are. When we apply this idea, we can see that the secant lines form a series of lines that are approaching some line (the tangent). If we get "infinitely close" to the tangent line, then we are as good as there!

Mathematically, this is usually expressed as follows:

$$f'(x) = \lim_{h \to 0} \frac{f(x+h) - f(x)}{h} \qquad (2\text{-}1)$$

Here $f'(x)$ is the derivative of the original mathematical function, $f(x)$. The derivative is taken with respect to x; that is, it is the change of the function $f(x)$ as the value of x changes near the point x. The term $f'(x)$ is also written as df/dx. It quantitatively indicates the small change in f divided by an infinitely small change (dx) in x.

If we look at Fig. 2-3B, the change in the value of the function $f(x)$ is given by the change $\Delta f = f(x_1) - f(x_2)$. The change in the value of x is $\Delta x = x_1 - x_2$. The slope of the line connecting the points $(x_1, f(x_1))$ and $(x_2, f(x_2))$ is, therefore, $[f(x_1) - f(x_2)] /(x_1 - x_2)$, or simply $\Delta f(x)/ \Delta x$. It can be shown, for example, that the slope of the tangent line (and hence the value of the derivative) of the function $y = x^2$ is $2x$. Thus, we can see that the slope of the curve at any point, is itself a function of x, the position of the point on the curve.

Quiz time! What problems arise when you attempt to numerically evaluate this derivative definition?

That's right. You remember from last chapter (you did read the last chapter, of course), that one of the largest sources of numerical error occurred when you subtracted two numbers that are close in value. Since we want h to be small (to get a good approximation of the derivative), then $f(x+h)$ will probably be only slightly different in value from $f(x)$. Hence, if you can ever avoid calculating derivatives numerically, then do so. Some times, you must calculate them, but whenever possible, find the analytical derivative [finding the equation for the derivative either by symbolic mathematics (Microsoft's muMATH symbolic manipulative package is highly recommended in this regard), or by looking it up in a table, such as that provided in Appendix B] and use it.

Sometimes, however, you will have to calculate those derivatives, so the best way to do that is to use the following central difference quotient formula:

$$f'(x) \approx \frac{f(x+h) - f(x-h)}{2h} \qquad (2\text{-}2)$$

This equation uses the values of either side of the point at which you want the derivative: $f(x-h)$ and $f(x+h)$. It is felt that this is more likely to be close to the derivative than using $f(x)$ as one point and $f(x+h)$ as the other. At any rate, this is the usual way for computed numerical derivatives, poor though it may be.

Program 2-1 calculates derivatives of the function defined in line 10. As mentioned before, the BASIC used is based on TRS-80 Disk BASIC, a Microsoft dialect. Appendix A has some conversion routines for functions not supported in other BASIC dialects. In particular, if your BASIC does not support the DEF FN function, then every time you see a DEF FN XX(xx,xx), then you must create à subroutine to specifically generate the function on which you wish to operate. For simplicity, let the variable carrying the value back from the subroutine have the same value as the name of the function. That is, let XX= the defined function so that XX will be the variable that returns the value. Be sure to end your subroutines with a RETURN statement, be very careful not to alter values that you don't want changed during the subroutine call, and pass the values correctly to the subroutine. An example of an altered program in this way is given in Program 2-2.

Program 2-1. Derivatives of the Sine Function

```
10 REM define your function in line 20
20 DEF FN F(X) = SIN(X)
30 DEF FN DF(X,H) = (FN F(X+H) − FN F(X−H))/2/H
40 INPUT"ENTER VALUE OF X FOR DERIVATVE";X
50 H=X*0.05
60 PRINT"F(X)=";FN F(X)
70 PRINT"DF/DX=";FN DF(X,H)
80 GOTO 40
```

Program 2-2. Program Without the DEF FN Function

```
10 REM define your function in 1000-1100
20 INPUT"ENTER THE VALUE OF X FOR DERIVATIVE";X1
30 H=X1*0.05
40 X=X1+H:GOSUB 1000:REM f(x+h)
40 F1=F
50 X=X1−H:GOSUB 1000:REM f(x−h)
60 DF=(F1−F)/2/H
70 X=X1:GOSUB 1000:REM f(x)
80 PRINT"F(X)=";F
90 PRINT"DF/DX=";DF
100 GOTO 20
110 END
1000 F=SIN(X):REM function defined here
1100 RETURN
```

BASIC INTEGRAL CALCULUS

An integral is the opposite of a derivative. That is, the integral of the derivative df/dx is the original function, f. The integral is therefore sometimes called the "antiderivative." It also has a geometric interpretation—that of the area under a curve. It is perhaps not intuitively obvious that the two definitions are the same. We will show their equivalence in just a bit.

The symbol dx is used to denote a very small change in x. In fact, it is the *limit* of Δx where Δx equals $(x_1 - x_2)$ as points x_1 and x_2 get closer and closer together. When they are infinitesimally close, that is, as close as they can get without coinciding, then $dx = \Delta x$. Put another way,

$$dx = \lim_{\Delta x \to 0} \Delta x = \lim_{x_1 \to x_2} (x_1 - x_2)$$

where x_1 and x_2 are on opposite sides of the point x on the curve.

An integral is just the opposite. The integral sign is just an elongated S ($\int$), originally indicating a sum. It is the sum of products involving derivatives at each point. The upper limit of the integration appears at the upper end of the integral sign; the lower limit of the integration appears at the lower end of the integral sign. They are the upper and lower limits for this summation. Unlike normal summation, indicated by a Greek sigma (Σ), the integral sums up infinitestially small parts. This can be easily seen in Fig. 2-4.

Fig. 2-4 is a graph of $g(x)$ versus x. We are defining $g(x) = f'(x)$, where $f'(x)$ is some arbitrary function, so we are losing no generality here. Note the rectangle in Fig. 2-4. What is the area of that rectangle? The area is the base times the height. The base is $\Delta x = B - A$ and the height is $g(a)$.

If we divide the entire curve area between the limits of $x=a$ and $x=b$, as in Fig. 2-5, then we see that the sum of the area of all these rectangles is a fair approximation of the area under the curve $g(x)$ between the limits of $x=a$ and $x=b$. But the rectangles are rather large. If we made them smaller, then we would have more rectangles, but they would result in an accurate approximation of the area. In fact, if we make them infinitesimally small, then they would add to exactly equal the area under the curve.

For a given function, we'll probably be interested in the area under the curve between two distinct values of x, bounding the area from the left and right, as in Fig. 2-6. These values of x that serve as boundaries are called the *limits of integration* and they define the

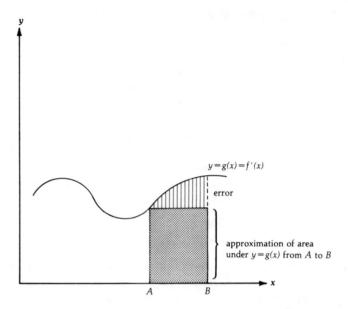

Fig. 2-4. A rectangle can be used to approximate the area under a curve.

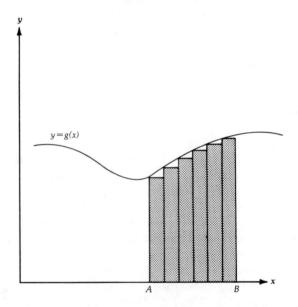

Fig. 2-5. Using small rectangles to better estimate the area under a curve.

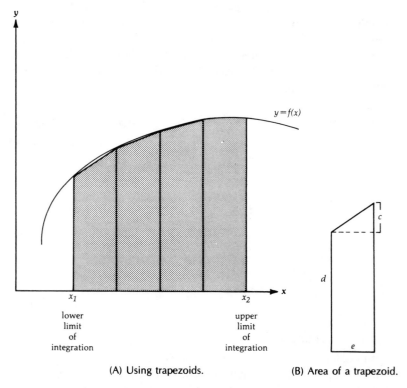

(A) Using trapezoids.

(B) Area of a trapezoid.

Fig. 2-6. Obtaining a better approximation of the area under a curve.

ends of the integration process. In Fig. 2-5 we are particularly interested in the shaded area bounded on the left by $x=a$ and on the right
of $x=b$. This is represented as

$$\text{area} = \int_a^b g(x)\, dx$$

which is read, "area equals the integral from a to b of $g(x)$."

Using the rectangle method described above, we can see that the
area under each rectangle is approximately $g(x)\Delta x$. Well, we previously defined $g(x) = f'(x)$, and we know that $f'(x) = df(x)/dx$, which is
often written df/dx. Therefore, by substitution, we have that the area is
$(df/dx)dx = df$. The integration sums all these df's (there are an infinite
number of them between a and b) and comes up with the answer: the
area under the curve from a to b.

FUNDAMENTAL THEOREM OF CALCULUS

Now to show the equivalence of the two definitions of the integral. (Don't worry too much if you have difficulty with this intuitive "proof." It isn't necessary to understand it in order for you to use the numerical methods of integration.) What is this infinite sum, written out? If we let z be the infinitesimally small increment in x [therefore, $df = f(x + z) - f(x)$], the sum is

$$\int_a^b f'(x)\ dx = [f(a+z)-f(a)] + [f(a+2z)-f(a-z)] + [f(a+3z)-f(a-2z)]$$
$$+ \dots + [f(b-z) - f(b-2z)] + [f(b) - f(b-z)]$$

Regrouping,

$$\int_a^b f'(x)\ dx = -f(a) + [f(a-z)- f(a-z)] + [f(a-2z)- f(a-2z)] + \dots$$
$$+[f(b-2z) -f(b-2z)] + [f(b-z) -f(b-z)] + f(b)$$

or, simply,

$$\int_a^b f'(x)\ dx = f(b) - f(a) \tag{2-3}$$

This relationship between the integral and the derivative is so important in calculus that it is known as the *Fundamental Theorem of Calculus*. And, in fact, we have just shown that finding the area under the curve of $g(x) = f'(x)$ is the same as integrating $f'(x)dx$.

The foregoing was just to help you understand what in the world an integral is. Numerically, there are a number of ways to calculate the integral. The better ones will be discussed later. There are two for which we will develop programs here: the rectangle method, discussed above, and the trapezoid method.

RECTANGLE METHOD OF NUMERICAL INTEGRATION

The rectangle method is just as we have outlined it above. If we want to integrate some function, $g(x)$, between two limits $x=a$ and $x=b$, then we divide area between the curve and the interval ab into a series of rectangles and add their areas. The area of each rectangle will be $g(x)\Delta x = g(c)(d-c)$, where c and d and the lower and upper limits for the rectangle in question. Then all you have to do is add them. Programs 2-3 and 2-4 do this. Program 2-3 uses a DEF FN, and

Program 2-4 uses a subroutine. If your BASIC does not support the DEF FN function, then these two programs may serve as a prototype for the conversion of a program containing the DEF FN to one that does not.

Program 2-3. Rectangular Integration With DEF FN

```
10 DEF FN F(X) = SIN(X)
20 INPUT"ENTER LOWER, UPPER LIMITS FOR INTEGRATION"; LOW,UP
30 INPUT"NUMBER OF RECTANGLES";R
40 SUM = 0:SIZE = (UP-LOW)/R
50 FOR 1 = LOW TO UP STEP SIZE
60    SUM = SUM + FN F(I)*SIZE
70 NEXT I
80 PRINT "THE INTEGRAL IS ";SUM
90 END
```

Program 2-4. Rectangular Integration With Subroutine

```
10 REM FN F(X) = DEFINED IN LINE 1000 AS SUBROUTINE
20 INPUT"ENTER LOWER, UPPER LIMITS FOR INTEGRATION"; LOW,UP
30 INPUT"NUMBER OF RECTANGLES";R
40 SUM = 0:SIZE = (UP-LOW)/R
50 FOR X = LOW TO UP STEP SIZE
60    GOSUB 1000
70    SUM = SUM + F*SIZE
80 NEXT I
90 PRINT "THE INTEGRAL IS ";SUM
100 END
1000 F = SIN(X)
1100 RETURN
```

When you use these programs, be sure that you know what the programs expect in terms of values. Programs 2-3 and 2-4 have the built-in BASIC function SIN(X). This function expects angles in radians, not degrees. If we wanted to integrate log x or tan x, we have to know that these functions have singularities (places where the function is not defined) and avoid these in our integration. The limits must be valid for the function being used. These programs expect a certain amount of sophistication on the part of their user. You may wish to error trap these programs by testing for illegal ranges or if a singularity falls within the otherwise legal range of values.

The SIN(X) and COS(X) algorithms used by most computers, such as the TRS-80, are only valid between the angles of $-\pi/2$ and $\pi/2$. The BASIC interpreter takes care of values outside this range by using a technique called *angle reduction*. The algorithm LOG(X) is, of course, undefined at X=0, and TAN(X) is undefined at an infinite number of points, where COS(X)=0, that is, integer multiples of $\pi/2$. Also, SQR(X) has problems when X<0 (BASIC doesn't know about complex numbers).

TRAPEZOID RULE FOR INTEGRATION

The rectangular approach is really not too accurate. The error of this method is due to the areas under the curve that are not enclosed by a rectangle (see Fig. 2-5). When you use the rectangle approach, you are assuming that the curve is fairly "flat." If you're not very far off, then the approximation shouldn't be too bad. But life is never that simple, you know!

Since we know the heights of the rectangles, we could easily make another assumption—that the curve between any two points is not a horizontal line, but instead a diagonal line connecting the sides of the two adjacent rectangles. This makes for a rectangle with a triangle for a top; this type of figure is called a *trapezoid*. The trapezoid approach is shown in Fig. 2-6A. As you can see, abandoning the horizontal tops for "sloped" ones makes the approximation to the real area much better.

The area of a trapezoid is easy to figure out and is given in Fig. 2-6B. If the trapezoid under a curve is bounded by $x=a$ below and $x=b$ above, then the area would be the area of the shorter side times the base $(b-a)$, giving the rectangle part, plus the area of the triangle, which would be 1/2 times the base (again $b-a$) times the height $(f(b) -f(a))$. This means that the area of each trapezoid is

$$\text{area} = f(a)\,(b-a) + \frac{1}{2}(b-a)\,(f(b) - f(a)) = \frac{1}{2}(f(b) + f(a))\,(b - a)$$

Fortunately, this is simple to program in BASIC and it is fairly accurate. Later, we will give methods with much greater accuracy, but this will suffice for now as the method of choice. In the program, the limits for the FOR loop are 1 and N−2. The reason is that we have rewritten the integration to be in a simpler form. If we let Q be the integral to be evaluated, then by the definition above we have

$$Q = \frac{1}{2}\sum_{i=2}^{n}(x_i - x_{i-1})[f(x_{i-1}) + f(x_i)]$$

If we let $h = \Delta x$ be a constant and a and b the lower and upper limits of integration, then $h = (b-a)/(n-1)$, and, for $i \geq 1$, $x_i = a + (i-1)h$, and $x_i - x_{i-1} = h$, so

$$Q = h\sum_{i=2}^{n}f(x_i) + \frac{h}{2}\left(f(x_i) + f(x_n)\right)$$

Program 2-5 does this. You will notice that the program is quite short, yet it does a lot!

Program 2-5. Trapezoidal Integration

```
10 DEF FN F(X) = EXP(SIN(X)): REM FUNCTION TO BE INTEGRATED
20 INPUT"ENTER THE LOWER AND UPPER INTEGRATION LIMITS"; LOW,
   UP
30 INPUT"ENTER THE NUMBER OF INTERVALS";N
40 SIZE = (UP-LOW)/(N-1):SUM = 0
50 FOR I = 1 to N-2
60    SUM = SUM + FN F(LOW+H*I)
70 NEXT I
80 SUM = (SUM + (FN F(LOW)+FN F(UP))/2)*H
90 PRINT "RESULT IS ";SUM
100 END
```

There is one more rather important topic that we need to discuss before we go on to other things. How does one choose an appropriate number of intervals?

On one level, it is simple. The more intervals you choose, the longer the integration will take to perform. Therefore, at first glance, it seems only to be a choice between accuracy and time. If you want your answer today, then don't use so many intervals; if you need great accuracy, you need only use a great many intervals. However, this is not quite true.

As budding numerical analysts, you realize, I'm sure, that there is a limit to the increase in accuracy with increased numbers of intervals. With the increase in intervals, the step size goes down. Each time, you're adding a very small number to what might be a very large number. Further, the increase in the number of computations adds roundoff error here too. *Sooner or later, any increase in the number of intervals will actually cause a decrease in the accuracy of the computed result; this is true of any iterated (repeated) process.* Normally, this is not too much of a problem, since under most circumstances, the number of intervals necessary to lose accuracy will be quite large, and you would lose patience before reaching it. Often, though, it occurs with only 1000 to 10,000 intervals. It depends on the nature of the function in the interval.

As an interesting exercise for the reader, consider the function

$$\text{erf}(t) = \frac{2}{\sqrt{\pi}}\int_{0}^{t} e^{-x^2}\, dx$$

It is called the Gaussian error function and a plot of the integrand e^{-x^2} generates a "normal" curve, as shown in Fig. 2-7. Notice that the upper limit of the curve is infinity and the lower limit is minus infinity. How do you integrate such a beast to find the best estimate of the true area?

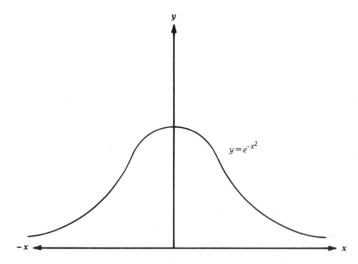

Fig. 2-7. Normal distribution curve.

When x is far from 0, the value of the function is very small, but it never reaches the value of 0. We can get as close as we like to 0 with e^{-x^2}, but we can never get there. Thus, we say that e^{-x^2} is *asymptotic* to 0. The trouble with integrating this function is that if you integrate between finite limits, then the area under the portion of the curve that you left out does amount to something, giving an error. On the other hand, if your intervals are large, then the trapezoids won't be good approximations of the shape of the curve, and you will get an error in that way. It appears to be a trade-off between using large enough size intervals to cover an appropriate amount of area of the curve, and using small enough intervals so that each trapezoid is a good approximation for the area under the curve. Your job, should you decide to accept it, is to find the best compromise between interval size and location of the upper and lower limits for integration with the constraint that you must use 20 intervals. Use the trapezoid program (Program 2-5) and adjust your limits to find the best approximation to the area under the curve. The true area is the square root of $\pi \approx$ 1.77245385.

CHAPTER 3

SOLVING EQUATIONS NUMERICALLY

How do you solve an equation, such as $2x - 4 = 3x + 1$?

Well, if you're like most folks, you "collect your terms," putting all the xs on one side and all the constants on the other, and then divide both sides of the equation by the coefficient of x to get the final result of -5. Computers generally cannot do things the way people do, although there are some symbolic algebraic systems that do work this way, such as REDUCE for main-frame IBM systems and muMATH from Microsoft for microcomputers. But these are written in special languages (LISP and LISP variants). FORTRAN, BASIC, Pascal, and other numerical languages can sometimes be coaxed into this sort of thing, but the programming is arduous at best. The numerical languages are designed to work differently.

BISECTION METHOD

There are many numerical techniques for solving equations. The simplest method is to put all the terms on one side of the equation so that it is now in the form $f(x) = 0$, and then find a zero crossing. A zero crossing is a place where the function equals zero (surprise, surprise). There are a couple of ways to look for zero crossings. One way would be to divide the interval that contains the solution into smaller intervals. Then check the values of the function at the end points of each of the smaller intevals. If the small intervals are small enough, and if the zero crossing does indeed occur in the area being searched, then the signs of the function at the end points of the smaller interval ought to be different. After all, if it is crossing zero during the interval, doesn't that mean that the sign of the function will change?

Once the solution (called the *zero*) of the function is located within one of these smaller intervals, then you repeat the process, dividing *that* interval into smaller intervals, etc., until you reach some criterion of closeness. This method is called the *bisection method*. Notice that this method will not find a zero unless:

1. the zero is in the larger interval being searched
2. the signs of the function are different at the end points of the smaller interval

There can be real problems satisfying these requirements. Often, you won't know where the solution is, so where do you look? One method would be to begin at zero and keep looking farther out until you find a zero crossing. But what about the other point?

The vertical bars in Fig. 3-1 indicate an interval used for looking for the zero crossing. Notice that there are, in fact, two zero crossings in that interval [C, D], so that the sign at the end points of the interval are the same. Let's put it this way: if the signs are different, then at least one zero crossing occurs in the interval. But if the signs are the same, there may be an even number of zero crossings in the interval. Life is tough all over, eh?

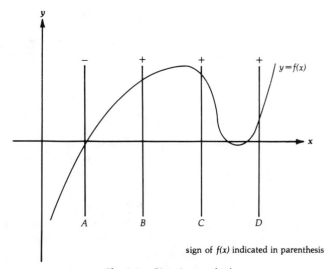

sign of $f(x)$ indicated in parenthesis

Fig. 3-1. Bisection method.

To mitigate these problems somewhat, often the physical reality of the situation giving rise to the problem to be solved indicates an approximate range for the answer—giving you an interval in which to look for the zero. Also, if the zero is in the interval, you need only use small enough subintervals to find it. While this can take a while, it will work. For example, if, after a single pass through the interval in question you do not find the zero, you can make a second pass with each subinterval one-half or one-fourth the size of the original subinterval, and so on.

Program 3-1 allows you to enter the equation to be solved in line 10 as a DEF FN, enter the end points of the interval to search, the criterion of convergence on the solution, and the number of subintervals in which to chop up the main interval. Then, it checks the signs of the function at each of the intervals. If it finds a zero crossing, then it takes that interval and chops it up into the same number of subintervals and repeats until the criterion of convergence is met.

The convergence criterion is a small number, such as 10^{-6}. This means that once the absolute value of the computed solution yields a value of the function less than the convergence criterion, then the program will stop iterating and display the answer. The particular function used in Program 3-1 is the arctangent function. Of course, you will enter your own function in line 10.

Program 3-1. Bisection Method

```
10 DEF FN F(X)=ATN(X)
20 REM FN ZERO returns −1 (TRUE) if the signs are different
30 REM and 0 (FALSE) if they are the same
40 DEF FN ZERO(X,Y)=(SGN(FN F(X))<>SGN(FN F(Y)))
50 REM FN CRIT(X) returns −1 (TRUE) if criterion met
60 REM otherwize returns a 0 (FALSE)
70 DEF FN CRIT(X)=(ABS(FN F(X))<CR)
80 INPUT"Enter the lower and upper end points of the interval";LO,UP
90 INPUT"Enter the number of subintervals";N
100 INPUT"Enter the convergence criterion";CR
110 IT=0:REM the number of iterations
120 STP=(UP−LO)/N:X=LO−STP
130 FOR I=1 TO N
140 IT=IT+1
150 X=X+STP:Y=X+STP
160 IF FN ZERO(X,Y) AND NOT (FN CRIT(X) OR FN CRIT(Y)) THEN
    PRINT"repeating . . . (X=";X;" y=";Y;")":LO=X:UP=Y:GOTO 120
170 IF FN ZERO(X,Y) AND FN CRIT(X) THEN PRINT"criterion met at ";
    X:PRINT"required ";IT; " iterations":PRINT"residual =";FN F(X):END
180 IF FN ZERO(X,Y) AND FN CRIT(Y) THEN PRINT"criterion met at ";
    Y:PRINT"required ";IT; " iterations":PRINT"residual =";FN F(Y):END
```

```
190 NEXT I
200 REM if it got here then it didn't meet the criterion
210 PRINT"No zero-crossings sighted"
220 GOTO 80
```

You will notice that I have a particular fondness for using functions to do things like find the zeros and compare for convergence. I believe that it makes programs easier to write and much easier to read. If you are a poor unfortunate whose BASIC does not support DEF FN, then see the appendix on BASIC program techniques for substituting subroutines for the DEF FN statements.

NEWTON-RAPHSON ITERATION

You can see that there are a couple of problems with the bisection method. Another problem is that it converges linearly. That means that you will add about 1 digit of accuracy per iteration loop, and that is a slow convergence. There is another method, called the Newton-Raphson iteration, which converges quadratically, adding almost two digits of accuray per iteration loop. We make a number of assumptions about the function in the equation to be solved, $f(x)=0$, including that it is differentiable. This means that $f(x)$ has a slope at each point and is continuous.

Since $f(x)$ is differentiable, then the tangent line of $f(x_0)$ is a good approximation to $f(x)$ as long as you're close to $x=x_0$. Since the tangent line is a good approximation of $f(x)$ in this neighborhood, then, the zero of the tangent line should be a good estimate of the zero of the function, right?

If we let $T(x)$ be the tangent line, and $f'(x)$ be the derivative of $f(x)$ with respect to x, then the equation for the tangent line is

$$T(x) = f'(x_0) (x - x_0) + f(x_0)$$

and in fact $f(x_0)=T(x_0)$ (since the line is tangent at x_0). This gives us a way to approximate the zero of $f(x)$. If $f(x_0) \approx 0$, then the zero of $T(x)$ ought to be an even better approximation. At the zero of $T(x)$ is

$$x_1 = x_0 - \frac{f(x_0)}{f'(x_0)}$$

If we use this zero, x_1, as a better approximation of the zero of $f(x)$, then we will be closer to the real zero, and we can find the zero of the tangent line at the new point to get $T(x)$ again, generating a value x_2, and so on until we have converged to the actual value of the zero of $f(x)$. This is graphically depicted in Fig. 3-2.

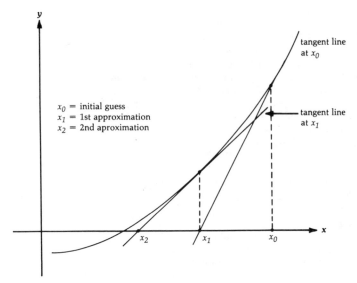

x_0 = initial guess
x_1 = 1st approximation
x_2 = 2nd aproximation

Fig. 3-2. Newton's method.

The Newton-Raphson iteration only converges when the point at which you evaluate the tangent line is reasonably close to the zero of the function $f(x)$. If not, then you are "too far away" from the zero, and you will either oscillate back and forth or actually diverge from the solution. The Newton-Raphson iteration method ought to converge within 10 to 20 iterations if it is ever going to converge.

Fig. 3-3 shows a situation in which the Newton-Raphson Iteration does not converge. The function is arctan x. Notice that we are so far from the zero of $f(x)$ that the zero of the tangent line is even farther away. On the next iteration, it is even farther away, and the method produces a rapidly diverging solution.

The Newton-Raphson method converges quite rapidly under most circumstances, though, and is one of the most popular methods around for solving equations. The iterative procedure is quite simple and is shown in Chart 3-1.

The scheme here is that we can use a previously computed value to generate a better approximation, ad infinitum. This is classically what is meant by the term "iteration."

Program 3-2. Newton-Raphson Iteration

```
10 REM Newton-Raphson Iteration
20 REM FN F(x) = the function to be solved.
```

```
30 REM FN DF(x) = the analytical derivatives
40 REM if DF is unknown then use:
50 REM FN DF(X,H)=(F(X+H) −F(X−H))/2/H
60 REM where H is some small value, like X/10
70 DEF FN F(X)=ATN(X):REM function to be solved
80 DEF FN DF(X)=1/(1+X²):REM analytical derivative
90 INPUT"Enter the first guess of the zero";X
100 INPUT"Enter the maximum number of iterations";CM
110 INPUT"Enter the convergence criterion";CR
120 FOR I=1 TO CM
130    X = X−FN F(X)/FN DF(X)
140      IF ABS(FN F(X))<CR THEN 200:REM convergence!
150 NEXT I
160 REM if it got here, then it didn't converge
170 PRINT"Convergence not met"
180 GOTO 90
190 REM convergence met!
200 PRINT"Convergence met at x=";X
210 PRINT"residual variance is ";FN F(X)
220 PRINT"Required ";I;" iterations":END
```

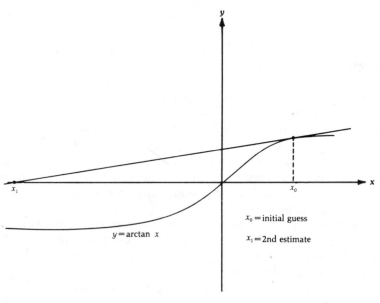

Fig. 3-3. Divergence of Newton-Raphson iteration.

As you can see, Program 3-2 is quite simple. You should use analytical derivatives when possible, either by deriving them or by using a table, such as that in the appendix. Sometimes, though, you will be forced to use numerical derivatives, and we have already discussed

Chart 3-1. Newton-Raphson Iterative Algorithm

1. $T(x) \approx f(x)$ around x_0, so the zero of $T(x) \approx$ the zero of $f(x)$.
2. $x_1 = x_0 - f(x_0)/f'(x_0)$
3. This is a better approximation of the real zero of $f(x)$ than was x_0, so we can use it in the same manner to generate an even better approximation, x_2:
$$x_2 = x_1 - f(x_1)/f'(x_1)$$
4. In general, the nth iteration produces the estimate:
$$x_n = x_m - f(x_m)/f'(x_m)$$
where $n = m + 1$.
5. Repeat from step 1 until convergence is achieved.

why that is always a dubious choice, but if the function doesn't have a convenient or easily obtainable derivative, then one does what one can. The increment for the derivative function described in line 50 of the Program 3-2 should be small compared with X, say X/10 or X/20.

Now for some examples. Let's compare the number of iterations and the accuracy of the bisection and Newton-Raphson methods with some sample equations. Table 3-1 shows some example functions for which the zeros have been found analytically and numerically via the bisection and Newton-Raphson methods. The same convergence criterion was used for both, and it is displayed as well.

Table 3-1. A Comparison Table of the Bisection and Newton-Raphson Methods

Function	Actual Solution	Convergence Criterion	Bisection Iterations	Residual	Newton-Raphson Iterations	Residual
$\sin x$	0	0.001	35	$-3.14E-4$	4	0
$\log x$	0	0.001	31	$-9.10E-4$	4	$-7.54E-6$
x^2+2x-3	$-3,1$	0.001	26	$4.52E-4$	4	$2.83E-6$
$\log(\exp(x))$	0	0.0001	45	$2.89E-7$	1	$1.92E-7$
$\sin(\cos(x^2))$	-7.1994	0.0001	28	$-5.99E-6$	4	0
$\arctan x$	0	0.0001	5	$-4.77E-7$	not convergent	

The bisection method required a lower and upper limit, and so -10 and 10 were used for functions 1, 2, 3, and 6. More appropriate limits were used for $\log x$ (namely, 0.0001 to 10) and $\sin(\cos x^2)$ (-8 to -6). For the Newton-Raphson method, a single number was chosen. Where possible, the upper limit for the bisection method was used, but this gave illegal function errors for some of the functions when the iteration exceeded the functions' normal limitations, so other first guesses had to be used that were actually closer to the correct guess. In the last function, arctan x, the procedure diverged quickly even if you were as far from zero as 1.00, but converged rapidly if you were quite close, such as 0.5.

These functions bring out an important point. The bisection method is slowly converging at best, but it usually will (eventually) get there. The Newton-Raphson iteration converges much more rapidly and accurately, but if you violate some assumptions, such as differentiability in the chosen interval or not being "sufficiently close," it may not converge at all.

For most functions, though, the Newton-Raphson method is amazingly fast in its convergence and is one of the most popular methods around for numerically solving equations.

SOLVING FOR ALL ROOTS

You may have noticed a problem with these methods. What about the other roots? Often, an equation will have many zeros; sin x has an infinite number, $x^2 + 2x - 3$ has two roots, etc. How about the more general problem of finding all roots?

Aye, there's the rub. For an arbitrary equation, it is an *extremely* difficult problem to find all roots. The methods given above will converge to what it considers the nearest root. There is, however, a class of equations for which you can find all the real roots—polynomials.

A *polynomial* is an expression of the form:

$$P(n,x) = ax^n + bx^{n-1} + \ldots + cx^2 + dx + e = 0 \qquad (3\text{-}1)$$

where n is the order of the equation, x is the variable, a, b, c, etc., are the constant coefficients of the terms. If r is a root, then the above equation must reduce to

$$P(n,x) = (x-r)(px^{n-1} + qx^{n-2} + \ldots + sx + t) = 0 \qquad (3\text{-}2)$$

We have used constants in Equation 3-2 that are different from the a, b, c, etc. In normal mathematical nomenclature, the a, b, c, and d terms would be reused with the understanding that the coefficients a, b, c, etc., in Equation 3-2 are not necessarily the same as in Equation 3-1.

The problem then reduces to one of finding the roots of the $(n-1)$th order polynomial:

$$P(n-1,x) = ax^{n-1} + bx^{n-2} + \ldots + cx + d = 0 \qquad (3\text{-}3)$$

You can see that since this is true regardless of n, we can successively remove the roots of the equation, resulting in a "remainder" equation having an order 1 less than the previous equation, until we have extracted all n roots. This process is called *synthetic division,* and it allows us to design a general method for finding all roots of a polynomial equation. Note that this assumes all the roots are real. If the root is imaginary or complex, then you will not be able to find it in this way. We'll burn that bridge when we come to it.

HORNER'S ALGORITHM

Program 3-3, Polysolver, uses a nested multiplication called Horner's algorithm and the Newton-Raphson iteration to find a root of a polynomial expression, uses synthetic division to reduce the order of the equation, and then repeats the process until roots are found, or until it is clear that the root cannot be found.

The array $A(i)$ holds the coefficient of the ith term of the polynomial. You are asked for the coefficients one at a time. After entering the coefficients, the equation will be displayed. You will then enter the workhorse part of the program.

First, you will be asked for the initial guess of the value of the root. The routine marked EVAL (line 500) then evaluates the root using Horner's algorithm. It may not be obvious that this is so, and accordingly, we will go through an example demonstrating that the methods are the same.

A short example is to evaluate the following polynomial:

$$P(3,x) = 3x^3 + 4x^2 + 5x - 6 \qquad (3-4)$$

which may be rewritten as

$$P(3,x) = x(5+x(4+3x)) - 6 \qquad (3-5)$$

As a first guess, let $x=2$, and let's now evaluate the result, "unfolding" the parentheses. See Table 3-2.

Similarly, the routine marked GETDERIV (line 550) calculates the derivative also using Horner's algorithm. The reason that this routine works is because

$$\frac{d(ax^n)}{dx} = anx^{n-1}$$

where a is a constant, n is a positive integer. Using the same example equation (and value for x) we can evaluate the derivative numerically, but still have a numerically correct value for the derivative. This is

Table 3-2. Horner's Algorithm vs. EVAL Subroutine

Horner's Method	EVAL Subroutine Method
. . . .	B(3)=A(3)=3
3x=6	B(2)=A(2)+B(3)*X=4+3*2=10
4+3x=10	B(1)=A(1)+B(2)*X=5+10*2=25
x(4+3x)=20	B(0)=A(0)+B(1)*X=-6+25*2=44
5+x(4+3x)=25	
x(5+x(4+3x))=50	
x(5+x(4+3x))-6=44	

because we are actually using the analytical derivative at the point of evaluation. The analytic derivative of Equation 3-4 is

$$d[P(3,x)] /dx = P(2,x) = 9x^2 + 8x + 5$$

and at $x=2$, this evaluates to be 57. Using the routine GETDERIV, we have

```
C=B(3)=3
C=B(2)+C*X=10 +3*2=16
C=B(1)+C*X=25 +16*2=57
```

The utility of this method lies in the ease with which both the derivative and the function can be evaluated. We used an array to evaluate the function because we wanted to keep the elements of $B(i)$ around for calculating the derivatives. We don't need to keep the various subtotals in GETDERIV, so we use a single constant rather than an array of numbers.

Note that the algebraic expression

$$A = 2 + A$$

and the BASIC program line

$$A = 2 + A$$

are not the same at all. The *algebraic expression* has no solution, but the BASIC program line is a *verb demanding the action "take the value in variable A and add 2 to it; then store that sum in variable A."* The difference is obvious to BASIC programmers because they are used to it, but a mathematician with no experience in computer languages would be confused. That is why we can use a single variable in GETDERIV and come out with the correct answer.

Program 3-3. Polysolver

```
10 REM POLYSOLVER
20 CLEAR 100:CLS:PRINT TAB(16);"POLYSOLVER"
```

```
30 DEFINT I-N
40 INPUT"Enter the order of the polynomial";N
50 N1=N:REM save the order for later use
60 DIM A(N),B(N),D(N),X(N)
70 FOR I=1 TO N
80     PRINT"Enter the coefficient of the ";N;"th term of X";
90     INPUT A(I):D(I)=A(I):REM save coefficients
100 NEXT I
110 INPUT"Enter the constant term";A(0):D(0)=A(0)
120 PRINT:PRINT"The polynomial to be solved is"
130 PRINT"P(";N;",X)=";
140 FOR I=N TO 1 STEP −1
150     PRINT A(I);"X↑";I; "+";
160 NEXT I
170 PRINT A(0)
180 INPUT"Enter convergence criterion";CR
190 INPUT"Enter max. number of iterations per root";MX
200 REM the work begins . . . .
210 FOR J=1 TO N1
220     PRINT"Initial guess of root #";J;:INPUT X:K=0
230     GOSUB 510:REM evaluate function
240     IF ABS(B(0))<=CN THEN 290:REM found root
250     IF C=0 THEN C=1E−4
260     IF K>MX THEN 610 ELSE K=K+1:REM # of iterations
270     X=X−B(0)/C:REM Newton's method
280     GOTO 230:REM repeat since not done
290     X(J)=X:REM save computed root
300     REM Reduce order of evaluation by synthetic division
310     FOR I=1 TO N
320         A(I−1)=B(I)
330     NEXT I:N=N−1
340     PRINT "root #";J;" is ";X
350     PRINT"required ";K;" iterations"
360 NEXT J
370 REM now correct for roundoff error using each
380 REM computed root as an estimate and resolving the
390 REM original equation
400 CLS:N=N1:FOR I=0 TO N:A(I)=D(I):NEXT I
410 FOR J=1 TO N:X=X(J):REM get computed root
420     GOSUB 510:REM evaluate function
430     IF ABS(B(0))<=CR THEN 460
440     X=X−B(0)/C
450     GOTO 420
460     X(J)=X:REM save corrected root
470     PRINT"Adjusted root =";X
480 NEXT J
490 END
500 REM **** EVAL ****
510 B(N)=A(N)
520 FOR I=N−1 TO 0 STEP −1
```

```
530     B(I)=A(I)+B(I+1)*X
540 NEXT I
550 REM **** GETDERIV ****
560 C=B(N)
570 FOR I=N-1 TO 1 STEP -1
580     C=B(I)+C*X
590 NEXT I
600 RETURN
610 REM did not converge
620 PRINT"root did not converge after ";K;" iterations."
630 PRINT"converged to ";X;" with residual of ";B(0)
640 INPUT"If answer is acceptable then enter 'Y' else enter 'N'";A$
650 IF A$="Y" THEN 290 ELSE 220
```

SYSTEM OF NONLINEAR EQUATIONS

The problem of finding roots for systems of linear equations is best performed by matrix manipulation techniques, such as matrix inversion with the sweep operator, or iterative matrix techniques, such as the Gauss-Seidel iteration method. Both of these methods are discussed in the next chapter. If the equations are nonlinear, however, these matrix methods do not apply, unless a suitable variable transformation can be found to make the system linear. For example, if you have the system of equations

$$\frac{3}{x} + \frac{9}{y} = 12$$

$$\frac{1}{x} - \frac{4}{y} = 0$$

Then you an substitute A for $1/x$ and B for $1/y$ to obtain a system linear in variables A and B. This system can then be solved through conventional matrix methods, and the solution obtained retransformed into the variables we originally had.

Often, though, these transformations are either difficult or impossible to obtain. We can, however, use the Newton-Raphson iteration method to find a solution iteratively to this problem. Suppose we have two functions in two variables, $f(x,y)$ and $g(x,y)$. These are similar to functions of one variable, except that instead of describing a curve in two-dimensional space (such as $f(x)=x^2$), they each describe a surface in three-dimensional space. The solution of the problem is the values of x and y for which the following are *both* true:

$$f(x,y) = 0$$

$$g(x,y) = 0$$

which defines an intersection of two surfaces.

Rather than deal with a tangent line to the curve, we are dealing with a tangent plane to the surface, but the analogy still holds. The equation for a plane tangent to the surface $f(x,y)$ at the point (x_1,y_1) is

$$z = f(x_1,y_1) + f_x(x_1,y_1)\ (x-x_1) + f_y(x_1,y_1)\ (y-y_1) \qquad (3\text{-}5)$$

where

$f_x(x,y)$ is the partial derivative of f with respect to x,
$f_y(x,y)$ is the partial derivative of f with respect to y.

A tangent plane to $g(x_1,y_1)$ can be similarly defined. The planes will intersect the xy plane, creating lines defined by the equations:

$$-f_1 = f_{x,1}(x-x_1) + f_{y,1}(y-y_1) \qquad (3\text{-}6)$$

$$-g_1 = g_{x,1}(x-x_1) + g_{y,1}(y-y_1) \qquad (3\text{-}7)$$

where

$$f_1 = f(x_1,y_1)$$

$$f_{x,1} = f_x(x_1,y_1)$$

$$g_1 = g(x_1,y_1)$$

$$g_{x,1} = g_x(x_1,y_1)$$

$$f_{y,1} = f_y(x_1,y_1)$$

$$g_{y,1} = g_y(x_1,y_1)$$

Equations 3-6 and 3-7 define lines that intersect the xy plane. These lines will intersect in a single point (if there is a unique solution) defined by the following two equations (perform the calculations by hand or with muMATH to verify these formulas):

$$x_2 = x_1 - \frac{f_1 g_{y,1} - g_1 f_{y,1}}{f_{x,1} g_{y,1} - g_{x,1} f_{y,1}} \qquad (3\text{-}8)$$

$$y_2 = y_1 - \frac{g_1 f_{x,1} - f_1 g_{x,1}}{f_{x,1} g_{y,1} - g_{x,1} f_{y,1}} \qquad (3\text{-}9)$$

These formulas should look remarkably similar to the formulas for the Newton-Raphson iteration of one variable. The formulas used for iteration are the same as for Equations 3-8 and 3-9, except that k is substituted for the current estimate of the solution:

$$x_{k+1} = x_k - \frac{f_k g_{y,k} - g_k f_{y,k}}{f_{x,k} g_{y,k} - g_{x,k} f_{y,k}} \qquad (3\text{-}10)$$

$$y_{k+1} = y_k - \frac{g_k f_{x,k} - f_k g_{x,k}}{f_{x,k} g_{y,k} - g_{x,k} f_{y,k}} \qquad (3\text{-}11)$$

The problem with this approach is calculating all the derivatives. Numerical derivatives can be used, but roundoff error makes your conclusions suspect. If you do use numerical derivatives, you should check your solutions by substituting them into the original equations. It is highly recommended that you use the analytical partial derivatives.

NOTE ON PARTIAL DERIVATIVES

For those of you who have never had any multivariate calculus, the process of taking a partial derivative of a function of several variables is identical with taking the derivative of a function of one variable. When you are taking the derivative of $f(x,y)$ with respect to x, you hold y constant; when you take the derivative with respect to y, you hold x constant. If $f(x,y)=2xy + 3x + 4y$, then the partial derivative f_x of f with respect to x is $2y+3$; the partial derivative f_y of f with respect to y is $2x + 4$.

Program 3-4 allows you to solve nonlinear systems to two equations with two unknowns.

Program 3-4. Newton's Method for Nonlinear Equations

```
10 REM Newton's method for 2 equations/2 unknowns
20 DEFINT I
30 REM Define test function to determine when converged
40 DEF FN TEST(X,Y,CR)=(ABS(FN F(X,Y))<CR) AND (ABS(FN G(X,Y))<CR)
50 REM Define your equations
60 DEF FN F(X,Y) = X↑2*Y↑2 −2*X*Y − X
70 DEF FN G(X,Y) = X + Y − 3
80 REM Define your derivatives
90 DEF FN FX(X,Y)= 2*X*Y↑2−2*Y−1: REM DF() W/ RESPECT TO X
100 DEF FN FY(X,Y)= 2*X↑2*Y−2*X:REM DF() W/ RESPECT TO Y
110 DEF FN GX(X,Y)=1:REM DG() W/ RESPECT TO X
120 DEF FN GY(X,Y)=1:REM DG() W/ RESPECT TO Y
130 REM Define your iterated equations
140 DEF FN DEN(X,Y)=FN FX(X,Y)*FN GY(X,Y) − FN GX(X,Y) *FN FY(X,Y)
    :REM DENOMINATOR IN ITERATION TERM
150 DEF FN NX(X,Y)=X − (FN F(X,Y)*FN GY(X,Y) − FN G(X,Y)*FN FY(X,Y))/
    FN DEN(X,Y)
160 DEF FN NY(X,Y)=Y − (FN G(X,Y)*FN FX(X,Y)− FN F(X,Y)*FN GX(X,Y))/FN
    DEN(X,Y)
170 REM Set up the system with default values
180 X=0:Y=0:IT=30:CR=1/128
190 INPUT"Enter your initial guess (X,Y)";X,Y
200 INPUT"Maximum number of iterations";IT
210 INPUT"Convergence criterion"; CR
220 REM iteration loop
```

```
230 FOR I=1 TO IT
240   X1 = FN NX(X,Y)
250   Y1 = FN NY(X,Y)
260   X = X1:Y = Y1
270   PRINT"Iteration ";I,"X=";X,"Y=";Y
280   REM Test for convergence
290   IF FN TEST(X,Y,CR) THEN GOTO 390:REM Done if true
300 NEXT I
310 REM Did not converge
320 PRINT"DID NOT CONVERGE!"
330 PRINT"Required ";I-1;" iterations"
340 PRINT"Converged to X=";X, "Y=";Y
350 PRINT"Residual from F(X,Y) IS";FN F(X,Y)
360 PRINT"Residual from G(X,Y) IS";FN G(X,Y)
370 END
380 REM CONVERGED!
390 PRINT"CONVERGED!"
400 PRINT"Required ";I" iterations"
410 PRINT"Converged to X=";X,"Y=";Y
420 PRINT"Residual from F(X,Y) IS";FN F(X,Y)
430 PRINT"Residual from G(X,Y) IS";FN G(X,Y)
440 END
```

Program 3-4 works on only two equations with two unknowns but it is derived from the Taylor series for two variables. We will deal with the Taylor series in more detail in Chapter 6 when we talk about approximations. To use Program 3-4 you must enter in the functions $f(x,y)$ and $g(x,y)$ as well as their derivatives with respect to x and y. In all, you must alter six program lines (lines 60, 70, 90, 100, 110, and 120). The other defined functions, TEST, NX, and NY, are defined in terms of the user-defined functions entered in those six lines, and need not be edited or changed. Be sure that you enter the program *exactly* as it appears. Of particular importance is that you must *not* forget to use FN F(X,Y) rather than F(X,Y). The former is the user-defined function, while the latter is an array (that doesn't exist in the program). Beginning programmers often make that particular mistake, and it can be difficult to track down.

After you have entered in the two functions, you must enter the initial guess (both X and Y values), the maximum number of iterations, and the convergence criterion. These all have default values, but they may not be appropriate for your application. The default values for x and y are 0,0; the default number of iterations is 30; the default convergence criterion is 1/128. The convergence criterion is how close the functions $f(x,y)$ and $g(x,y)$ must *both* be to zero before the program thinks it has found the answer. The program displays the iteration number and current estimates of x and y for each iteration. At the end, the computed values for x and y are displayed, along with the number of iterations required, and the residual values for f(x,y) and g(x,y). The residual values are the values for the functions evaluated at the computed roots. If the function converged, these residuals ought to be close to zero.

Although we discourage the use of numerical derivatives in the Newton-Raphson method, particularly applied to systems of equations, sometimes it cannot be avoided. Program 3-5 will perform the method without requiring you to enter the derivatives.

Program 3-5: Newton's Method With Numerical Derivatives

```
10 REM Newton's method for 2 equations/2 unknowns
20 DEFINT I
30 REM Define Test function
40 DEF FN TEST(X,Y,CR)=(ABS(FN F(X,Y))<CR) AND (ABS(FN G(X,Y))<CR)
50 REM Define your equations
60 DEF FN F(X,Y) = X↑2*Y↑2 − 2*X*Y − X
70 DEF FN G(X,Y) = X + Y − 3
80 REM Define numerical derivatives
90 DEF FN FX(X,Y)=(FN F(X+H,Y)−FN F(X−H,Y))/2/H: REM DF() W/ RE-
      SPECT TO X
100 DEF FN FY(X,Y)=(FN F(X,Y+H)−FN F(X,Y−H))/2/H: REM DF () W/ RE-
      SPECT TO Y
110 DEF FN GX(X,Y)=(FN G(X+H,Y)−FN G(X−H,Y))/2/H: REM DG() W/ RE-
      SPECT TO X
120 DEF FN GY(X,Y)=(FN G(X,Y+H)−FN G(X,Y−H))/2/H: REM DG() W/ RE-
      SPECT TO Y
130 REM Define your iterated equations
140 DEF FN DEN(X,Y)=FN FX(X,Y)*FN GY(X,Y) − FN GX(X,Y)*FN FY(X,Y)
      :REM DENOMINATOR IN ITERATION TERM
150 DEF FN NX(X,Y)=X − (FN F(X,Y)*FN GY(X,Y) −FN G(X,Y)*FN FY(X,Y))/
      FN DEN(X,Y)
160 DEF FN NY(X,Y)=Y −(FN G(X,Y)*FN FX(X,Y) − FN F(X,Y)*FN GX(X,Y))/FN
      DEN(X,Y)
170 REM set up the system with default values
180 X=0:Y=0:IT=30:CR=1/128:H=1/128
190 INPUT"Enter your initial guess (X,Y)";X,Y
200 INPUT"Maximum number of iterations";IT
210 INPUT"Converge criterion";CR
220 INPUT"Enter step size for numerical derivatives";H
230 REM Iteration loop
240 FOR I=1 TO IT
250    X1 = FN NX(X,Y)
260    Y1 = FN NY(X,Y)
270    X = X1:Y = Y1
280    PRINT"Iteration ";I,"X=" ;X,"Y=";Y
```

```
290    REM Test for convergence
300    IF FN TEST(X,Y,CR) THEN GOTO 400:REM done if TRUE
310 NEXT I
320 REM DID NOT CONVERGE
330 PRINT"DID NOT CONVERGE!"
340 PRINT"Required ";I-1;" iterations"
350 PRINT"converged to X=";X,"Y=";Y
360 PRINT"residual from F(X,Y) IS";FN F(X,Y)
370 PRINT"residual from G(X,Y) IS";FN G(X,Y)
380 END
390 REM CONVERGED!
400 PRINT"CONVERGED!"
410 PRINT"Required ";I" iterations"
420 PRINT"Converged to X=";X,"Y=";Y
430 PRINT"Residual from F(X,Y) IS";FN F(X,Y)
440 PRINT"Residual from G(X,Y) IS";FN G(X,Y)
450 END
```

Program 3-5 uses numerical derivatives. To use this program, you need only enter the functions F(X,Y) and G(X,Y) in lines 60 and 70—no other editing needs to be done. There is an additional parameter to be defined when you run the program. You will be asked for the step size for the numerical derivative. This value, H in the program, is used with the finite-difference equations to calculate the derivatives numerically. Use this program with care. For many systems it will work fine; but for others it will fail miserably.

One application of the approach of systems of equations is to solve for complex roots of equations. Complex numbers are of the form

$$z = x + iy$$

where i is the square root of -1, x and y are both real. A function of the form

$$f(z) = g(z) + ih(z) \qquad (3\text{-}12)$$

where g and h are real-valued functions for all z can be solved easily using the Newton-Raphson iteration method. The derivative of $f(z)$ can be found from the Cauchy-Riemann equations for analytic functions:

$$f'(z) = g_x + ih_x = h_y - ig_y \qquad (3\text{-}13)$$

Therefore the Newton-Raphson method for complex functions can be written as shown in Chart 3-2.

You can then write the function $f(z)$ as two functions: a real function $g(z)$ and an imaginary function $ih(z)$. Variables x and y are both

Chart 3-2. Newton-Raphson Method for Complex Functions

$$x_{n+1} = x_n - \frac{gh_y - hg_y}{g_xh_y - g_yh_x} \qquad (3\text{-}14)$$

$$y_{n+1} = y_n - \frac{hg_x - gh_x}{g_xh_y - g_yh_x} \qquad (3\text{-}15)$$

real valued, but since $z=x+iy$, you can find a complex root of this form by using Program 3-4 or Program 3-5.

For example, suppose you want to solve the complex quadratic function

$$f(z) = z^2 - 2z - 2 = 0 \qquad (3\text{-}16)$$

which is the same as

$$f(z) = (x+iy)^2 - 2(x+iy) - 2 = 0 \qquad (3\text{-}17)$$

Separating this into real and imaginary parts, we get

$$f(z) = (x^2 - y^2 - 2x - 2) - 2iy(x - 1)$$

This may be rewritten:

$$g(x,y) = x^2 - y^2 - 2x - 2 = 0 \text{ (real part)} \qquad (3\text{-}18)$$

$$h(x,y) = -2y(x-1) = 0 \text{ (imaginary part)} \qquad (3\text{-}19)$$

$$g_x(x,y) = 2x - 2 \qquad (3\text{-}20)$$

$$g_y(x,y) = -2y \qquad (3\text{-}21)$$

$$h_x(x,y) = -2y \qquad (3\text{-}22)$$

$$h_y(x,y) = -2(x-1) \qquad (3\text{-}23)$$

Table 3-3. Solving Complex Functions Using Real Analogs

Complex Function of $z=x+iy$	Real Functions of x and y
$f(z) = \exp(z) + a$	$g(x,y) = \exp(x)\cos y + a$ $h(x,y) = \exp(x)\sin y$
$f(z) = a/z$	$g(x,y) = ax/(x^2+y^2)$ $h(x,y) = ay/(x^2+y^2)$
$f(z) = (z+a)^2$	$g(x,y) = x^2-y^2+2ax+a^2$ $h(x,y) = 2y(x+a)$

This problem can now be submitted to Program 3-3 or Program 3-4 to determine the solutions $(1,-1)$ and $(1,1)$, which correspond to the complex answer $1-i$ and $1+i$. The functions to be solved are $g(x,y)$ and $h(x,y)$, given by Equations 3-18 and 3-19, and the partial derivatives are given in Equations 3-20 to 3-23. This method provides a simple means for finding the root of complex functions.

Table 3-3 provides some sample complex functions and the same functions written in the $g(x,y)$, $h(x,y)$ format, so you may go through the task of computing the $g(x,y)$ and $h(x,y)$ functions for practice and to make sure you understand the process. The first function uses the relationship $\exp(iy) = \cos y + i \sin y$, which can be proved by evaluating the Taylor series for the three functions.

Chapter 4

VECTORS AND MATRICES

A *matrix* is a rectangular array of numbers. If the matrix has *m* rows and *n* columns, then it is called an "*m* by *n* matrix." A vector is a "skinny" matrix, i.e., a matrix which has 1 row and *n* columns: a 1 by *n* matrix.

The number of dimensions represented in a vector is called its *order*. A five-dimensional vector would be something like $(1,2,-4,9,1/2)$. An *n*-dimensional vector has *n* numbers that uniquely define it in *n*-dimensional space.

One can think of a vector as a collection of scalars (real numbers). One can, in turn, think of a matrix as a collection of vectors. A matrix may have *m* rows and *n* columns. If you take *m* vectors from an *n*-dimensional space and group them together, then you would have an *m* by *n* matrix. Vectors and matrices are specific examples of a general mathematical construct called a *tensor*. A scalar quantity is a zeroth-order tensor; a vector is a first-order tensor; a matrix is a second-order tensor. See the progression?

Here is an example 3 by 4 matrix:

$$\text{rows} \begin{pmatrix} 1,1 & 1,2 & 1,3 & 1,4 \\ 2,1 & 2,2 & 2,3 & 2,4 \\ 3,1 & 3,2 & 3,3 & 3,4 \end{pmatrix}$$

columns

You can see, in the above matrix, the "coordinates" of each element. The element 1,1 is in the first row and first column; the element 2,4 is in the second row and the fourth column, etc. If the number of rows equals the number of columns, then the matrix is said to be *square*.

The main diagonal of a matrix includes the elements 1,1; 2,2; 3,3; and so on. If the matrix is symmetrical about the main diagonal (i.e., the "upper triangle" is a mirror image of the "lower triangle"), then the matrix is said to be *symmetrical*. The matrix

$$\begin{pmatrix} 2 & 0 & -1 & 8 \\ 0 & .5 & \pi & 3 \\ -1 & \pi & 4 & 16 \\ 8 & 3 & 16 & 1 \end{pmatrix}$$

is square and symmetrical.

Vectors and matrices are useful in all sorts of applications, such as solving systems of linear equations, a topic we will discuss at length later in this chapter, as well as statistics, Markov analysis, and lists of other seemingly unrelated problems. There are certain rules about how you can manipulate these critters.

For simplicity, when we are referring to a vector or matrix, we will boldface it and make it lowercase or uppercase, respectively, e.g., **C** (uppercase) is a matrix and **a** (lowercase) is a vector. When we are referring to a specific element of a vector or a matrix, the name will not be boldfaced, but the subscripts will identify the element in question, such as $a_{1,2}$ is the element of matrix **A** in the first row and the second column. For a vector, we might use z_n to identify the nth element of the vector **z**.

There are a number of important rules for both vector and matrix manipulation. We will discuss and present BASIC subroutines for each of these.

MATRIX ARITHMETIC

For vectors as well as matrices, the rules for addition and subtraction are the same. First, the two matrices must have the same number of rows and columns. The sum of two vectors or matrices is a vector or matrix with the same number of rows and columns. Each element of the resultant matrix is the sum (or difference in the case of subtraction) of the corresponding elements in the original matrices, i.e., the element in the ith row and jth column of the resultant matrix **C** = **A** + **B** is defined as

$$c_{ij} = a_{ij} + b_{ij}$$

For example, you can see how the elements are combined in the matrix addition problem below:

$$3 \text{-----------} + 2 \text{-----------} = 5$$

$$\begin{array}{ccc} \uparrow & \uparrow & \uparrow \end{array}$$

$$\begin{pmatrix} 3 & 0 & 5 \\ 7 & 6 & 9 \\ 2 & 9 & -8 \end{pmatrix} + \begin{pmatrix} 2 & 7 & 6 \\ 1 & -3 & 18 \\ 2 & 9 & 6 \end{pmatrix} = \begin{pmatrix} 5 & 7 & 11 \\ 8 & 3 & 27 \\ 4 & 18 & -2 \end{pmatrix}$$

$$\begin{array}{ccc} \downarrow & \downarrow & \downarrow \end{array}$$

$$9 \text{-----------} + 9 \text{-----------} = 18$$

Here the sums $a_{11} + b_{11} = c_{11}$ and $a_{32} + b_{32} = c_{32}$ have been shown specifically.

Vectors have a special operation called a *dot product*. The result is a scalar (real number). Each corresponding element pair in both matrices is multiplied together and these are summed up to give what is called the dot (or "scalar") product.

If vectors $\mathbf{a} = (1,3)$ and $\mathbf{b} = (4,5)$, then the dot product $\mathbf{a} \cdot \mathbf{b} = (1 \times 4 + 3 \times 5) = 19$. In general,

$$\mathbf{a} \cdot \mathbf{b} = \Sigma \, a_i \, b_i$$

where a_i and b_i are the elements of $\mathbf{a}$ and $\mathbf{b}$.

The length of a vector, also called the *norm* of the vector, is the square root of the sum of each element squared:

$$\text{length of } \mathbf{a} = \|\mathbf{a}\| = \sqrt{\Sigma \, a_i^2}$$

If vector $\mathbf{a} = (1,2,3)$ then its norm is $(1^2 + 2^2 + 3^2)^{1/2} = (1+4+9)^{1/2} = (15)^{1/2} = 3.873$. This is the length of the vector.

Multiplying matrices is not as easy as one might think. To multiply matrix $\mathbf{A}$ by matrix $\mathbf{B}$, the number of columns of $\mathbf{A}$ must equal the number of rows in $\mathbf{B}$. If $\mathbf{A}$ is m by n, and $\mathbf{B}$ is n by p, then the product $\mathbf{AB} = \mathbf{C}$ will be an m by p matrix. Each element of C is defined by

$$c_{ij} = \sum_{k=1}^{k=n} a_{ik} \, b_{kj}$$

where

c_{ij} is the element in the ith row and jth column of $\mathbf{C}$,
a_{ik} is the element in the ith row and kth column of $\mathbf{A}$,
b_{kj} is the element in the kth row and jth column of $\mathbf{B}$.

It would be good practice for you to carry our the multiplication example below:

$$\begin{pmatrix} 1 & 2 \\ 3 & 4 \end{pmatrix} \begin{pmatrix} 5 & 6 \\ 7 & 8 \end{pmatrix} = \begin{pmatrix} 1 \cdot [5] + 2 \cdot [7] & 1 \cdot [6] + 2 \cdot [8] \\ 3 \cdot [5] + 4 \cdot [7] & 3 \cdot [6] + 4 \cdot [8] \end{pmatrix} = \begin{pmatrix} 19 & 22 \\ 43 & 50 \end{pmatrix}$$

Implicit, though perhaps not obvious, in this definition is the fact that matrix multiplication is not commutative, that is, in general $\mathbf{AB} \neq \mathbf{BA}$. Thus it becomes important to make a distinction between *premultiplication* and *postmultiplication*. If you premultiply $\mathbf{B}$ with $\mathbf{A}$, you have the product $\mathbf{AB}$. If you postmultiply $\mathbf{B}$ with $\mathbf{A}$, you have the product $\mathbf{BA}$. For familiarity, we suggest that you perform the following multiplications by hand (or, you can cheat and use Program 4-1, MATRIX). See that the results are not the same?

$$\begin{pmatrix} 1 & 1 \\ 0 & 1 \end{pmatrix} \begin{pmatrix} 0 & 0 \\ 1 & 1 \end{pmatrix} = \begin{pmatrix} 1 & 1 \\ 1 & 1 \end{pmatrix}$$

and

$$\begin{pmatrix} 0 & 0 \\ 1 & 1 \end{pmatrix} \begin{pmatrix} 1 & 1 \\ 0 & 1 \end{pmatrix} = \begin{pmatrix} 0 & 0 \\ 1 & 2 \end{pmatrix}$$

Of course, there are some particular matrices for which $\mathbf{AB} = \mathbf{BA}$, but these are special cases. In particular, a matrix of the form

$$\begin{pmatrix} a & 0 & 0 \\ 0 & a & 0 \\ 0 & 0 & a \end{pmatrix} \qquad \text{(matrix 4-1)}$$

will produce products with square matrices (of the same order) in which multiplication is commutative. If the as in matrix 4-1 are all equal to 1, then it is called the *identity matrix*, $\mathbf{I}$. In this case $\mathbf{IA} = \mathbf{AI} = \mathbf{A}$. If the as are not equal to 1, then it is called a *scalar matrix*, because multiplication by this matrix is the same as multiplying the matrix $\mathbf{A}$ by a scalar value, a.

Program 4-1, MATRIX, is a simple one with defined subroutines demonstrating the programming for these simple matrix-arithmetic operations.

Program 4-1. Matrix Arithmetic

```
10 REM Matrix Arithmetic
20 PRINT"MATRIX ARITHMETIC PROGRAM":DEFINT I-N
30 REM DEFINE MATRIX A
40 INPUT"Enter the rows and columns for matrix A";AR,AC
50 DIM A(AR,AC)
60 PRINT"ENTER THE ELEMENTS . . ."
70 FOR I=1 to AR
80     FOR J=1 TO AC
90         PRINT"Enter element for row =";I; " and column =";J;
100        INPUT A(I,J)
110 NEXT J,I
120 REM DEFINE MATRIX B
```

```
130 INPUT"Enter the rows and columns for matrix B";BR,BC
140 DIM B(BR,BC)
150 PRINT"ENTER THE ELEMENTS . . ."
160 FOR I=1 TO BR
170   FOR J=1 TO BC
180     PRINT"Enter element for row =";I; "and column =";J;
190     INPUT B(I,J)
200 NEXT J,I
210 REM PRESENT OPTIONS
220 PRINT"OPTIONS:"
230 PRINT"1. DISPLAY A            2. DISPLAY B"
240 PRINT"3. ADD A CONSTANT       4. MULTIPLY BY A CONSTANT"
250 PRINT"5. A * B                6. B * A"
260 PRINT"ENTER OPTION . . .";
270 INPUT OP:ON OP GOTO 290,320,370,470,570,590
280 GOTO 220
290 GOSUB 1000:GOTO 310
300 GOSUB 1100
310 FOR I=1 TO ROW
320   FOR J=1 TO COL
330     IF FL=1 THEN PRINT A(I,J); ELSE PRINT B(I,J);
340 NEXT J,I
350 PRINT"PRESS (ENTER) TO RETURN TO MENU"
360 INPUT FL:GOTO 220
370 REM ADD A SCALAR
380 INPUT"1. ADD TO MATRIX A      2. ADD TO MATRIX B";FL
390 INPUT"ENTER SCALAR";SC
400 ON FL GOSUB 1000,1100
410 FOR I=1 TO ROW
420   FOR J=1 TO COL
430     IF FL=1 THEN A(I,J)=A(I,J)+SC: PRINT A(I,J);
440     IF FL=2 THEN B(I,J)=B(I,J)+SC: PRINT B(I,J);
450 NEXT J,I
460 INPUT"PRESS (ENTER) TO RETURN TO MENU";FL:GOTO 220
470 REM MULTIPLY BY A SCALAR
480 INPUT"1. MULTIPLY MATRIX A      2. MULTIPLY MATRIX B";FL
490 INPUT"ENTER SCALAR";SC
500 ON FL GOSUB 1000,1100
510 FOR I=1 TO ROW
520   FOR J=1 TO COL
530     IF FL=1 THEN A(I,J)=A(I,J)* SC: PRINT A(I,J);
540     IF FL=2 THEN B(I,J)=B(I,J)* SC:PRINT B(I,J);
550 NEXT J:PRINT:NEXT I
560 REM A * B
570 M=AR:N=AC: N1=BR:P=BC: FL=1:DIM AB(M,P):IF N1=N THEN 610
580 PRIN"INCOMPATIBLE MATRICES":GOTO 220
590 M=BR:N=BC:N1=AR: P=AC:FL=2:IF N<>N1 THEN 580 ELSE DIM
    BA(M,P)
600 REM THE FUN BEGINS
610 FOR I=1 TO M
```

```
620   FOR J=1 TO P:SUM=0
630     FOR K=1 TO N
640       IF FL=1 THEN SUM=SUM+A(I,K)*B(K,J)
650       IF FL=2 THEN SUM=SUM+B(I,K)*A(K,J)
660     NEXT K
670   IF FL=1 THEN AB(I,J)=SUM:PRINT AB(I,J);
680   IF FL=2 THEN BA(I,J)=SUM:PRINT BA(I,J);
690 NEXT J,I
700 INPUT"PRESS (ENTER) TO RETURN TO MENU";FL:GOTO 220
1000 ROW=AR:COL=AC:FL=1: PRINT"MATRIX A":RETURN
1100 ROW=BR:COL=BC:FL=2: PRINT"MATRIX B":RETURN
```

GAUSSIAN ELIMINATION AND THE SWEEP OPERATOR

Matrices are mathematically peculiar items. You may perform operations called *transformations* to change a matrix from one form to another. Some matrices are easier to deal with than others. Generally, you want to transform a "problem" matrix into a "solution" matrix. When you transform one matrix into a simpler equivalent matrix, you have *reduced* the matrix into a more useful form. Two examples we will deal with in detail are the calculation of the determinant of a matrix and determining the solution of a system of linear equations.

The method of matrix reduction we will use is the ever popular method known as Gaussian (or Gauss-Jordan) elimination. The use of Gaussian reduction relies on these important transformations of matrices:

1. Multiply each element of one row by a nonzero constant.
2. Interchange any two rows.
3. Add one row to another.

The multiplication of a row by a constant, or adding of one row to another within a matrix, etc., is called an *elementary row operation*. The effect of these elementary row operations can be reproduced by first performing the operation on the identity matrix and then using the altered identity matrix as a premultiplier. The identity matrix is analogous to the scalar multiplicative identity element. Simply put, the multiplicative identity element for scalars is 1, since $A \times 1 = A$, regardless of what A is. The identity matrix is similar. It turns out (you can try this by hand or by using program 4-1 to check it), that the identity matrix of a given size is simply a square matrix with all elements being zeros except that there are 1s in the main diagonal. For example:

$$\begin{matrix} \mathbf{I} & \textbf{times} & \mathbf{A} & = & \mathbf{A} \end{matrix}$$

$$\begin{pmatrix} 1 & 0 & 0 \\ 0 & 1 & 0 \\ 0 & 0 & 1 \end{pmatrix} \quad \begin{pmatrix} a_{11} & a_{12} & a_{13} \\ a_{21} & a_{22} & a_{23} \\ a_{31} & a_{32} & a_{33} \end{pmatrix} = \begin{pmatrix} a_{11} & a_{12} & a_{13} \\ a_{21} & a_{22} & a_{23} \\ a_{31} & a_{32} & a_{33} \end{pmatrix}$$

Mathematical methods that use these elementary row operations to zero out selected elements of a matrix are called *Gaussian elimination methods*.

For example, let's reduce the following matrix, **A.** This 3 by 3 matrix is *augmented* with a 3 by 3 identity matrix:

$$\begin{matrix} \mathbf{A} & \textbf{aug} & \mathbf{I} & = & \mathbf{A}^{+} \end{matrix}$$

$$\begin{pmatrix} 3 & 0 & 1 \\ 0 & 1 & 0 \\ 2 & 0 & 1 \end{pmatrix} \text{AUG} \begin{pmatrix} 1 & 0 & 0 \\ 0 & 1 & 0 \\ 0 & 0 & 1 \end{pmatrix} = \begin{pmatrix} 3 & 0 & 1 & 1 & 0 & 0 \\ 0 & 1 & 0 & 0 & 1 & 0 \\ 2 & 0 & 1 & 0 & 0 & 1 \end{pmatrix}$$

We can perform elementary row operations on $\mathbf{A}^{+}$ to reduce it to the form in which the left-hand side is an identity matrix and the right-hand side is a new matrix. We shall see later that the right-hand side of the transformed matrix is actually the inverse of **A.**

First, let's reduce the first column so that the left-hand side is the first column of an identity matrix, i.e., consists of the elements 1, 0, 0. The operations necessary to perform this transformation are as follows.

Reduction 1:

1. Multiply the first row by 1/3, making it (1 0 1/3 1/3 0 0).
2. Subtract 2 times the new first row from the third row, making the third row (0 0 1/3 −2/3 0 1).

The result of this transformation is the matrix:

$$\begin{pmatrix} 1 & 0 & 1/3 & 1/3 & 0 & 0 \\ 0 & 1 & 0 & 0 & 1 & 0 \\ 0 & 0 & 1/3 & -2/3 & 0 & 1 \end{pmatrix}$$

Note that column 2 is already of the required form, so we needn't transform it, and we can go on to reduction 3.

Reduction 3:

1. Subtract row 3 from row 1 and put it in row 1, making row 1 (1 0 0 1 0 −1).
2. Multiply row 3 times 3 and put it in row 3, making row 3 (0 0 1 −2 0 3).

The result after reduction 3 is:

$$\begin{pmatrix} 1 & 0 & 0 & 1 & 0 & -1 \\ 0 & 1 & 0 & 0 & 1 & 0 \\ 0 & 0 & 1 & -2 & 0 & 3 \end{pmatrix}$$

The transformed matrix is now in the form we wanted; the left half is the identity matrix, and we did it by the Gaussian elimination method. The 3 by 3 matrix on the right half of the transformed matrix is the *inverse* of the original matrix, **A**. The meaning and uses of the inverse matrix will be discussed shortly.

For a square matrix of order n, we transform the kth row, each row at a time, in order to put an identity matrix in the kth column. Put another way, the kth column is the one of interest, even though the kth row is where the actual operations are performed. To indicate this "interest," we call the kth row the *pivotal row* and the element in the kth row and kth column (in the main diagonal) is called the *pivotal element*. Since we know that we are transforming a row and column at a time, we need not keep them in storage, as we did above. Memory storage is, after all, quite a valuable item on microcomputers. In this way, we can avoid using the extra space taken up by the augmented matrix A^+ above.

The end result of the row reduction is to replace the ith column by a column from an identity matrix, and the $(i+n)$th column of the augmented matrix becomes the column we want (where the matrix **A** is of order n). Rather than stick in the column from the identity matrix (which we don't want anyway), we'll just throw it away and keep the $(i+n)$th column in the ith column, thus bypassing the necessity of creating a matrix twice as large for the augmented matrix. In the above example, the matrices produced after each of the two reductions are:

$$
\underset{\textbf{A}}{\begin{pmatrix} 3 & 0 & 1 \\ 0 & 1 & 0 \\ 2 & 0 & 1 \end{pmatrix}} \xrightarrow[\text{reduction 1}]{} \begin{pmatrix} 1/3 & 0 & 1/3 \\ 0 & 1 & 0 \\ -2/3 & 0 & 1/3 \end{pmatrix} \xrightarrow[\text{reduction 3}]{} \underset{\textbf{A}^{-1}}{\begin{pmatrix} 1 & 0 & -1 \\ 0 & 1 & 0 \\ -2 & 0 & -3 \end{pmatrix}}
$$

Note that the ith column (where i is the reduction number) does not contain the identity matrix, as in the augmented matrix example above, but instead, it has the ith column from the right half of the augmented matrix. In 1964, A. Beaton published his paper, *The Use of Special Matrix Operators in Statistical Calculus* (Educational Testing Service. RB 64-51, Princeton, NJ), and in it he introduced the concept of a *sweep operator* to describe these special row transformations. The sweep operator is merely a name for a group of tasks performed in a specific algorithmic implementation of Gaussian elimination. It is nothing especially new, but it helps break up the procedure of performing Gaussian elimination into a somewhat smaller step that can be iterated.

Both the sweep operator and garden-variety Gaussian elimination require that the matrix is nonsingular. This means *that no row is a linear combination of other rows, and that the same is true for columns.* For example, consider the following two matrices.

$$A = \begin{pmatrix} 3 & 6 \\ 1 & 2 \end{pmatrix} \quad B = \begin{pmatrix} 1 & 2 & 3 \\ 0 & 1 & 4 \\ 2 & 5 & 10 \end{pmatrix}$$

Matrix **A** is singular because the second row (1 2) is a simple multiple of the first row (3 6). Matrix **B** is also singular because the third row is a linear combination of the first two. In fact row 3 is two times row 1 plus row 3.

If you have a singular matrix, the Gaussian methods will not work, because you lack enough information to solve the system uniquely. If it is a coefficient matrix for solving simultaneous linear equations, then there is no unique solution; if you are trying to find the determinant, then the determinant is zero. The inverse of this matrix does not exist.

Given that a matrix is nonsingular, these methods may still fail if the rows are not in the appropriate order. Because the above method does not check to see if they are in the correct order, it is called *naive Gaussian elimination.* Fortunately, there are two easy ways to deal with this problem. Both are variants on the same theme.

Since you can interchange rows and columns of a matrix, you can search for the proper pivotal element in the row, and, if it is not the *i*th row, then switch the *i*th column with the column containing the pivotal element. This method is a little slow because entire columns are moved, but it is useful if memory is tight, since it requires no additional storage. The other method is to keep an array of pointers to the pivotal elements, but not actually move the columns around. It is faster than the move-the-entire-column approach, particularly for large matrices that are mostly not in the correct order, but it does require more space for the array of pointers. On small problems, you normally may use either method because memory is sufficient and the time saved by using the array of pointers is not great.

Since the two methods are so similar, we'll only implement one of them, the method of the index array. Surprisingly enough, despite the rather large literature available to the lay computerist via magazines and books, none of these has yet implemented the sweep operator combined with the scaled partial pivot described here. Before we present a program to do this, we'll develop a reason for doing this— solving systems of linear equations.

SYSTEMS OF LINEAR EQUATIONS

The solution of systems of linear equations is a very important one in science and engineering. In general, such a system may be written as one of n equations and n unknowns:

$$a_{11}x_1 + a_{12}x_2 + \ldots + a_{1n}x_n = b_1$$

$$a_{21}x_1 + a_{22}x_2 + \ldots + a_{2n}x_n = b_2 \tag{4-1}$$

$$a_{n1}x_1 + a_{n2}x_2 + \ldots + a_{nn}x_n = b_n$$

This system may arise from a number of physical problems, such as the simple problem below:

> A given quantity of 6-percent alcohol solution (generic beer) is consumed by a college freshman with a 0.01-percent alcohol concentration, resulting in a blood alcohol content of 1.72 percent. If he drank 2/3 liter less of the beer, his blood alcohol would be a 1.27-percent alcohol solution. What is his blood volume and how much liquid did he drink?

This is perhaps an artificial example (unless, of course, you're in a college fraternity), but it is well suited to be solved as a system of simultaneous linear equations. At the end of this chapter, we will discuss some word problems that describe some physical problems, and ways to solve them. There are a vast number of physical situations that give rise to problems that are linear in more than one variable. Gaussian elimination is one powerful method to solve these.

Equations 4-1 may be rewritten to be a matrix equation:

$$
\underset{\textstyle \mathbf{A}}{\begin{pmatrix} a_{11} & a_{12} & \cdots & a_{1n} \\ a_{21} & a_{22} & \cdots & a_{2n} \\ \cdot & \cdot & & \cdot \\ \cdot & \cdot & & \cdot \\ \cdot & \cdot & & \cdot \\ a_{n1} & a_{n2} & \cdots & a_{nn} \end{pmatrix}}
\overset{\textstyle \text{times}}{}
\underset{\textstyle \mathbf{x}}{\begin{pmatrix} x_1 \\ x_2 \\ \cdot \\ \cdot \\ \cdot \\ x_n \end{pmatrix}}
\overset{\textstyle =}{}
\underset{\textstyle \mathbf{b}}{\begin{pmatrix} b_1 \\ b_2 \\ \cdot \\ \cdot \\ \cdot \\ b_n \end{pmatrix}}
$$

The matrix **A** is called the *coefficient* matrix, since it contains the coefficients of the variables; **x** is the variable vector, since it contains the variables; **b** is called the constant vector because it holds the constants from the system of equations. We have now written the problem in the form of a *matrix equation*.

There are two straightforward methods for solving the system, that is, determining the values for the xs that make all the equations true at the same time. The first method is to divide by the matrix **A** on both sides of Equation 4-2 to get the **x** matrix all by itself on the left of the equation. Although division by matrices is really not defined, we can multiply the *inverse* of matrix **A**. The inverse of matrix **A** is defined to be the matrix that makes the following statement true:

$$A^{-1}A = I$$

where
  A^{-1} is the inverse of **A**,
  I is the identity matrix.

The inverse of the matrix **A** is much like the multiplicative inverse of a scalar a. This is, you may recall from algebra, $1/a$, since $a(1/a) = 1$. The problem of finding the solution is then reduced to the problem of inverting the coefficient matrix and postmultiplying it with the coefficient vector **b**. If the problem does not have a unique solution, the inverse does not exist.

The other method is to create, from Equations 4-1, an n by $n+1$ matrix containing the coefficient matrix and the constant vector put into the same matrix:

A aug b

$$\begin{pmatrix} a_{11} & a_{12} & \ldots & a_{1n} & b_1 \\ a_{21} & a_{22} & \ldots & a_{2n} & b_2 \\ & \cdot & \cdot & \cdot & \\ & \cdot & \cdot & \cdot & \\ & \cdot & \cdot & \cdot & \\ a_{n1} & a_{n2} & \ldots & a_{nn} & b_n \end{pmatrix}$$

The method used in this case is simple as well. Using the Gaussian elimination techniques, reduce the left n by n portion of the matrix to an identity matrix. The vector in the $(n+1)$th column will be the solutions of the x's. The main point here is that an equivalent system of equations is a system of equations that have the same solutions. This method reduces the complexity of the system to an equivalent system until it is of the form:

$$\begin{pmatrix} 1 & 0 & 0 & \cdots & 0 & s_1 \\ 0 & 1 & 0 & & 0 & s_2 \cdot \\ \cdot & & \cdot & & \cdot & \cdot \\ \cdot & & & & \cdot & \cdot \\ 0 & 0 & 0 & \cdots & 1 & s_n \end{pmatrix}$$

which corresponds to the system of equations:

$$1x_1 + 0x_2 + \ldots + 0x_n = s_1$$

$$0x_1 + 1x_2 + \ldots + 0x_n = s_2$$

$$\begin{array}{ccc} \cdot & \cdot & \cdot \\ \cdot & \cdot & \cdot \\ \cdot & \cdot & \cdot \end{array} \qquad (4\text{-}3)$$

$$0x_1 + 0x_2 + \ldots + 1x_n = s_n$$

Equations 4-3 are obviously the most useful equivalent system of equations, since we can immediately tell from it the value of each of the variables that make the system true. There are other methods, such as the use of a determinant, for solving systems of equations, but we'll use these two.

Program 4-2 solves a system of equations by either of these two methods. It uses variable array dimensioning; that is, notice that the DIM statement uses a variable, N, for dimensioning the size of the array. Some BASICs do not have that capability. In that case, use the largest value that you will probably ever use. If the largest system you will ever solve is one with ten equations and 10 unknowns, then substitute a 10 for the N in the DIM statement.

Program 4-2 uses the naive Gaussian elimination method implemented by the sweep operator described above. This means that rather than have the program do a "Forward" elimination pass and then a "Backwards" elimination pass, the sweep operator does both at once. The program is not error trapped for singular systems. If you wish to catch these errors, use a line such as

```
15 ON ERROR GOTO 2000
  and
2000 PRINT"ERROR CODE ";ERR/2+1:REM TRS-80 specific code
2010 IF ERR/2+1=11 THEN PRINT"Singular system"
2020 END
```

The error code for a divide-by-zero error is 11, and line 2010 will catch that. A singular system will manifest itself in a divide-by-zero error most often. The program expects that the number of equations and the number of unknowns is the same—that is, the system is neither overdefined nor underdefined.

Program 4-2. Simultaneous Equations

```
10 REM simultaneous equation solver
20 INPUT"Enter the number of equations";N
30 INPUT"Method: 1. inversion 2. augmented matrix";ME
40 IF ME=2 THEN 500
```

```
50 REM ** inversion method **
60 DIM A(N,N),X(N),B(N)
70 REM input system parameters
80 FOR K=1 TO N
90    PRINT"Enter the constant term for equation";K
100   INPUT B(K)
110      FOR J=1 TO N
120      PRINT"Enter coefficient eq. ";K;" variable ";J
130      INPUT A(K,J)
140 NEXT J,K
150 REM invert the matrix A with sweep operator
160 REM this uses 'naive' elimination
170 FOR K = 1 TO N
180   PIVOT = A(K,K):REM assuming pivot is correct
190   FOR L = 1 TO N:REM divide row by pivot
200    A(K,L)=A(K,L)/PIVOT
210   NEXT L
220   A(K,K)=1/PIVOT:REM adjust pivot element
230   REM now sweep the other rows to reduce this
240   REM column to a unit vector
250   FOR J = 1 TO N
260    IF (A(J,K) = 0) OR (J=K) THEN 360
270    MU = A(J,K)
280    FOR L = 1 TO N
290     A(J,L) = A(J,L) − A(K,L) * MU
300    NEXT L
310    A(J,K) = A(J,K) − MU
320    REM adjust element in
330    REM pivotal column—this is the same as replacing
340    REM the unit vector in this columns as per sweep
350    REM operator methodology
360   NEXT J,K
370 REM A() now contains the inverse of the original
380 REM coefficient matrix. Now, multiply A*B
390 FOR L = 1 TO N
400   FOR K = 1 TO N
430    X(L) = X(L) + A(L,K)*B(K)
440 NEXT K,L
450 PRINT"The solution is "
460 FOR I=1 TO N
470   PRINT "X(";I;")=";X(I)
480 NEXT I
490 END
500   REM augmented matrix method
510 DIM A(N,N+1)
520 REM input system parameters
530 FOR K=1 TO N
540   PRINT"Enter the constant term for equation";K
550   INPUT A(K,N+1)
560   FOR J=1 TO N
```

```
570     PRINT"Enter coefficient eq. ";K;" variable ";J
580     INPUT A(K,J)
590     NEXT J,K
600 REM now sweep this augmented matrix
610     FOR K = 1 TO N
620     PIVOT = A(K,K):REM assuming pivot is correct again
630     FOR L = 1 TO N+1:REM divide row by pivot
640       A(K,L)=A(K,L)/PIVOT
650     NEXT L
660     REM now sweep the other rows to reduce this
670     REM column to a unit vector
680     FOR J = 1 TO N
690       IF (A(J,K) = 0) OR J=K THEN 740
700       MU = A(J,K)
710       FOR L = 1 TO N+1
720         A(J,L) = A(J,L) − A(K,L) * MU
730       NEXT L
740     NEXT J,K
750     REM solution is in the (n+1)st column
760     PRINT"The solution is "
770     FOR I=1 TO N
780       PRINT "X(";I;")=";A(I,N+1)
790     NEXT I
800     END
```

For example, if you have a system of linear equations:

$$2x_1 + 3x_2 - x_3 = 5$$

$$x_1 - 2x_2 + 5x_3 = 12 \qquad (4\text{-}4)$$

$$x_1 + x_2 + x_3 = 6$$

you would answer the question of the number of equations with a 3. Then you would be asked, for each equation in turn, the value of the constant term (5 for the first equation, for example), and then the coefficients (2, 3, and -1 for the first equation). The answer is computed and displayed. For Equations 4-4 $x_1 = 1$, $x_2 = 2$, and $x_3 = 3$.

SCALED PARTIAL PIVOTING

There are a couple of flaws in Program 4-2 when it is applied to real problems. First, consider the system of equations below:

$$0x_1 + 1x_2 = 3$$

$$2x_1 + 0x_2 = -1$$

The system is in already reduced form, although somewhat out of order. The solution to the problem is obvious, $x_2 = 3$ and $x_1 = -1/2$. But Program 4-2 cannot solve this problem, because it will try to pivot on the elements of the main diagonal of the coefficient matrix, and these values are zeros. One solution here would be to test for a zero in the main diagonal, and if one exists, then switch rows.

Consider the next problem:

$$0.0001x_1 + 1.00x_2 = 1$$

$$1.00x_1 + 1.00x_2 = 2$$

If solved directly, many computers will give the result $x_1=0$ and $x_2=1$. Obviously, this is far from the correct answer, even though there are no zeroes in the diagonal. A problem such as this is called *ill-conditioned*, because it does not conveniently lend itself to generating a correct solution. If we rewrite the problem:

$$1.00x_1 + 1.00x_2 = 2$$

$$0.0001x_1 + 1.00x_2 = 1$$

Then we can compute the answer $x_1 = 1, x_2=1$. Although this answer is not exact, it is a vast improvement. The method we will use to circumvent ill-conditioned matrices is called *scaled partial pivoting*.

The main idea behind this method is that matrices that are dominated by their diagonals are better conditioned matrices than matrices that are dominated by off-diagonal elements. We determine the dominant values to use for the pivots in each row and, through this, hope to determine more accurately the true answers to the problem. We will use a separate array, $L(i)$, which is the *index array*. This array will keep track of the pivotal elements for us. A scale factor for each row is determined by

$$s_i = \max |a_{ij}|$$

Thus s_i is the maximum value in the ith row of the matrix **A**, and all the s_i are kept in the array **S**. We start out assuming that the matrix is in proper order; accordingly, the **L** array contains the numbers 1 to n in order. That is, $L(1)=1$, $L(2)=2, \ldots , L(n)=n$. As we begin the Gaussian elimination, we test each row to determine where the pivot is. We do this by choosing the row having the largest value for the ratio

$$|a_{i1}/s_i|$$

Once we have determined the ratio for the pivot, if the pivoting element is different from the main diagonal element, we exchange the two indices in the index array. This means that we need only exchange the two numbers in the index array and not the entire rows in the coefficient matrix.

The DEF FN MAX of line 20, Program 4-3, defines a function that returns the greater of two values. FN MAX(1,2) will return a 2, for example. If your BASIC does not support the DEF FN feature, then whenever you see it, substitute the definition of the function in the line (with appropriate substitution of parameters, of course). Alternatively, you may replace it with an IF-THEN statement to return the larger of two statements.

Program 4-3. Simultaneous Equations With Pivoting

```
10 REM simultaneous equation solver version 2
20 DEF FN MAX(A,B)=-(A)B)*A-(B)=A)*B
30 INPUT"Enter the number of equations";N
40 INPUT"Method: 1. Inversion 2. Augmented matrix";ME
50 IF ME=2 THEN 620
60 REM ** inversion method **
70 DIM A(N,N),X(N),B(N),L(N),S(N)
80 REM input system parameters
90 FOR K=1 TO N
100    PRINT"Enter the constant term for equation";K
110    INPUT B(K)
120    FOR J=1 TO N
130       PRINT"Enter coefficient eq. ";K;" variable ";J
140       INPUT A(K,J)
150    NEXT J,K
160 REM invert the matrix A with sweep operator
170 REM this uses partial scaled pivoting
180 REM set up the arrays
190 FOR K=1 TO N:L(K)=K:S(K)=0
200 FOR J=1 TO N
210    S(K) = FN MAX(S(K),ABS(A(K,J)))
220 NEXT J,K
230 REM now perform the operations
240 FOR K = 1 TO N
250 RM=0
260 FOR I=K TO N
270 R=ABS(A(L(I),K))/S(L(I))
280 IF R>RM THEN J=I:RM=R
290 NEXT I
300 REM now switch pivot indicies
310 LK=L(J):L(J)=L(K):L(K)=LK
320 PIVOT = A(LK,K)
330    FOR I = 1 TO N:REM divide row by pivot
340       A(LK,I)=A(LK,I)/PIVOT
```

70

```
350    NEXT I
360    A(LK,K)=1/PIVOT:REM adjust pivot element
370    REM now sweep the other rows to reduce this
380    REM column to a unit vector
390    FOR I = 1 TO N
400      IF (L(I)=LK) THEN 500
410      MU = A(L(I),K)
420        FOR J = 1 TO N
430          A(L(I),J) = A(L(I),J) - A(LK,J) * MU
440        NEXT J
450      A(L(I),K)=A(L(I),K)-MU
460      REM adjust element in
470      REM pivotal column—this is the same as replacing
480      REM the unit vector in this columns as per sweep
490      REM operator methodology
500    NEXT I,K
510    REM A() now contains the inverse of the original
520    REM coefficient matrix. Now, multiply A*B
530    FOR I = 1 TO N
540      FOR K = 1 TO N
550        X(I) = X(I) + A(L(I),L(K))*B(K)
560    NEXT, K,I
570    PRINT"The solution is "
580    FOR I=1 TO N
590      PRINT "X(";I;")=";X(I)
600    NEXT I
610    END
620    REM augmented matrix method
630 DIM A(N,N+1),L(N),S(N)
640 REM input system parameters
650 FOR K=1 TO N
660    PRINT"Enter the constant term for equation";K
670    INPUT A(K,N+1)
680    FOR J=1 TO N
690      PRINT"Enter coefficient eq. ";K; variable ";J
700      INPUT A(K,J)
710    NEXT J,K
720 REM now sweep this augmented matrix
730 REM set up the arrays
740 FOR K=1 TO N:L(K)=K:S(K)=0
750 FOR J=1 TO N
760 S(K) = FN MAX(S(K),ABS(A(K,J)))
770 NEXT J,K
780    FOR K = 1 TO N
790 RM=0
800 FOR I=K TO N
810 R=ABS(A(L(I),K))/S(L(I))
820 IF R>RM THEN J=I:RM=R
830 NEXT I
840 REM now switch pivot indicies
```

```
850 LK=L(J):L(J)=L(K):L(K)=LK
860   PIVOT = A(LK,K)
870   FOR I = 1 TO N+1:REM divide row by pivot
880     A(LK,I)=A(LK,I)/PIVOT
890   NEXT I
900   REM now sweep the other rows to reduce this
910   REM column to a unit vector
920   FOR I = 1 TO N
930     IF L(I)=LK THEN 980
940     MU = A(L(I),K)
950     FOR J = 1 TO N+1
960       A(L(I),J) = A(L(I),J) − A(LK,J) * MU
970     NEXT J
980   NEXT I,K
990   REM solution is in the (n+1)th column
1000    PRINT"The solution is "
1010    FOR I=1 TO N
1020      PRINT "X(";I;")=";A(L(I),N+1)
1030    NEXT I
1040    END
```

In the real world, one rarely has equations dumped on one's lap. Usually, one begins with a problem and the creation of the equations in part of the creative effort put forth by the problem solver. While teaching mathematics to college students, I have found that almost without exception, this is the part they liked and understood the least. The dreaded beast has an innocuous name:

WORD PROBLEMS

I emphasize word problems when I teach because these are practical problems; problems that you might meet out there in the real world; problems that require answers that aren't in the back of the book. They require creative effort to solve. Most of the effort goes to restating the problem in mathematical terms—equations.

Consider the college fraternity problem earlier in this chapter. The problem was:

> A given quantity of 6-percent alcohol solution (generic beer) is consumed by a college freshman with a 0.01-percent alcohol concentration, resulting in a blood alcohol content of 1.72 percent. If he drank 2/3 liter less of the brew, his blood alcohol would be 1.27 percent. What is his blood volume, and how much beer did he drink?

The main task to solving the problem is to set up the equations. Once set up, solving the problem is a mere rote task. Rote tasks can be tedious, but require little creative effort. In this problem the task is to set up an equation, or system of equations, with unknowns. What do we want to know?

We want to know the volume of blood in the college freshman and the amount of beer he drank. Let V be the blood volume and B be the amount of beer. We know that blood volume is well regulated, so that the fluid portion of the beer is not retained but rather, ah, recycled. However, we'll assume that the alcohol content of the urine is the same as that of the blood, so that the alcohol is diluted (or is it the blood that's being diluted?) into a volume equal to the sum of the blood's volume and the volume of the beer. The first statement says that the freshman has a blood content of 0.01 percent, he drinks a 6-percent alcohol solution and raises his blood content to 1.72 percent. Expressed in an equation, this statement is equivalent to

$$0.01V + 6B = 1.72 (V + B) \qquad (4\text{-}5)$$

which reduces to

$$1.71V - 4.28B = 0 \qquad (4\text{-}6)$$

The second statement is that if he drank less beer (2/3 liter less to be exact), then his blood alcohol would have been only 1.27 percent. Expressed in an equation, this is the same as

$$0.01V + 6(B-2/3) = 1.27(V + B - 2/3) \qquad (4\text{-}7)$$

or

$$1.26V - 4.73B = -3.153$$

The system to be solved is, therefore,

$$1.71V - 4.28B = 0$$
$$1.26V - 4.73B = 3.153 \qquad (4\text{-}8)$$

This problem can be submitted to Program 4-3 to be solved (the freshman has 5 liters of blood and he drank 2 liters of beer).

Another class of problems are the work problems that drive college freshmen to drink in the first place. For example:

> Joe and Mortimer can do a job together in 32 hours. If Joe works alone for 8 hours and then Mortimer finishes the job in 80 hours, how many hours would it take for each to do the job alone?

I'll wait until you've finished pouring your drink.

This problem is really not that difficult either. The unit of "job" is 1 if the job is done. If we let x be the number of hours it takes Joe to do the job alone and y be the number of hours it takes Mortimer to do the job alone, then the amount of the job by Joe while working with Mortimer (first statement) is $32/x$. The amount of work done during the same time by Mortimer is $32/y$. Therefore, our first equation is

$$\frac{32}{x} + \frac{32}{y} = 1$$

since they did get the job done. The second statement describes a different equation. Since Joe worked alone for 8 hours and then left, the amount of the job that he did would be $8/x$. Mortimer came alone and worked overtime (by himself) for the next 80 hours; so the amount of the job he got done would be $80/y$. The equation describing this state of affairs is

$$\frac{8}{x} + \frac{80}{y} = 1$$

We can't use the simultaneous linear equation solver because it expects linear equations! On the other hand, we can make up two new variables, a and b, defined by

$$A = \frac{1}{x} \quad \text{and} \quad B = \frac{1}{y}$$

and this generates the solvable system:

$$32A + 32B = 1$$

$$8A + 80B = 1$$

This system can be submitted to Program 4-3. Remember that the answer you want is the reciprocal of the computed answer.

Now a problem for you to solve. Don't look ahead until you've solved it.

> Sally and Sue can do a job together in 16 hours. If Sally and Sue work together for 6 hours, and then Sue finishes in 20 hours, how many hours would it take for each to do the job alone?

Setting this one up is easy, since it is a variation of the previous problem. The system of equations to be solved is:

$$16A + 16B = 1$$

$$6A + 26B = 1$$

where A and B are the reciprocals of the values we really want.

You can see that the difficult part of these problems really is one of translation. The problem needs to be translated fron English to mathematics. Once this translation is performed, the solution is relatively easy to find.

ITERATIVE MATRIX METHODS

The matrix methods dealt with so far are quite easy to program, fast, and useful. For some problems, however, they contain too much roundoff to be of use. This is usually either because the coefficient matrix is ill-conditioned, or it is "sparse," meaning that most of the off-diagonal elements are zeros. When this is the case, an iterative method is called for. An iterative matrix method works similarly to the iterative schemes we have used for other purposes, such as solving equations with the Newton-Raphson iteration. We make several calculated guesses about the answer, each better than the last, until we are as accurate as necessary.

The method we will discuss in this section is known as the Gauss-Seidel method. The specific application of this iterative approach is to the familiar problem of solving simultaneous equations. If we let $\mathbf{x}$ be the solution vector in the matrix equation

$$\mathbf{Ax} = 4$$

we will generate a series of these solution vectors, $\mathbf{x}_0$, $\mathbf{x}_1$, and so on. The kth iteration will produce the solution vector $\mathbf{x}_k$. The initial estimate of the solution may be arbitrary, or if the matrix $\mathbf{A}$ is dominated by the diagonal elements, one can make an initial guess,

$$x_i = a_{ii}/b_i$$

where the a_{ii} are the diagonal elements of $\mathbf{A}$.

The system of equations we have been discussing may be written in the form:

$$x_1 = (b_1 - a_{12}x_2 - \ldots - a_{1n}x_n)/a_{11}$$

$$x_2 = (b_2 - a_{21}x_1 - \ldots - a_{2n}x_n)/a_{22}$$

$$\vdots \tag{4-9}$$

$$x_n = (b_n - a_{b1}x_1 - \ldots - a_{n-1,n}\,x_{n-1})/a_{nn}$$

Each time we perform this iteration, we obtain a new complete vector $\mathbf{x}$. We can see that when the matrix $\mathbf{A}$ is dominated by the diagonal elements, then b_k/a_{kk} is not too bad as a first guess. The expression

$$r_i = b_i - a_{i1}x_1 - \ldots - a_{in}x_n$$

gives the residuals, r_i. A method that reduces these residuals to zero during the course of the iteration is called a *relaxation method*. The Gauss-Seidel method is a relaxation method, because the difference between the substituted values in the sum of the x's times their coefficients and the constant terms in each equation is reduced to zero.

The standard method of coding an iterative algorithm like this is to use the previous values for all the elements of the vector **x** in calculating the next vector estimate. The convergence can be speeded up by using the current values of the latest calculated x's in creating each estimate. This method of implementation is called the *Gauss-Seidel method*.

The Gauss-Seidel method converges quickly, if it converges at all. It will converge if the coefficient matrix is diagonally dominant, or if it can be put into a diagonally dominant form through pivoting. But what does the term "convergence" mean?

The convergence test we will use is an "absolute test," in which the difference between successive **x** vectors is tested. When this difference grows so small that it is less than some predetermined constant (i.e., the residuals get close to zero), then we have converged. We will want to make sure that this is true for the largest residual, since if it has met the convergence criterion, then all the others will.

In Program 4-4, SEIDEL, we use the Gauss-Seidel method to solve a system of linear equations. We do use the same scaled partial pivoting strategy we used for the Gauss-Jordan elimination method earlier. The program displays the vector of estimates, **x**, during each iteration. Since we are using partial scaled pivoting, we may rewrite the typical equation from the system described in Equations 4-9 by

$$x_{L(k)} = [b_{L(k)} - \sum_{\substack{j=1 \\ j \neq k}}^{n} a_{L(k),j}\, x_j]/\, a_{L(k),k}$$

It is most appropriate to use when the coefficient matrix is largely composed of zeros or when ill-conditioning makes the Gauss-Jordan method unusable because of roundoff error. The Gauss-Seidel method does not accumulate roundoff error because each estimate depends only on the previous estimate and not on a series of calculations, as does the Gauss-Jordan estimate.

We would like to know whether the Gauss-Seidel method will converge or not, before we run the program. We provide a test for convergence within Program 4-4. The program reports whether or not it meets the test, and then continues with the attempt to solve the system regardless of the test's outcome. There is only one simple convergence test for this method: the diagonal dominance test. If the coefficient matrix passes this test, then the iteration will converge. If it fails the test, then it may or may not converge. The test is

$$|a_{ii}| > \sum_{\substack{j=1 \\ j \neq i}}^{j=n} |a_{ij}|$$

where the vertical bars denote the absolute value (or ABS).

This may be thought of as a "very diagonally dominant test" because it is true only if the absolute value of each diagonal element is greater than the sum of the absolute values of the off-diagonal elements in that row. Of course, "diagonal" suggests that we are using naive methods. Since we use partial scaled pivoting, the pivotal element may not be the diagonal. However, the name is common, so we will continue to use it.

Program 4-4. Gauss-Seidel Iteration With Partial Scaled Pivoting

```
10 REM                SEIDEL/PIV
20 REM Simultaneous Equation Solver by Gauss-Seidel method
30 REM with Partial Scaled Pivoting
40 DEFINT J,K,I,L:CR=1/256:IM=10:IT=0: :U$="####. #### "
50 DEF FN MAX(A,B)=-(A>B) *A-(B=>A) *B
60 REM FN DN Tests if convergence criterion met
70 DEF FN DN(A,B)=(A<=B)
80 REM
90 REM input routine
100 REM
110 INPUT"Enter the number of equations";N
120 DIM A(N,N),X(N),B(N),R(N),S(N),L(N)
130 FOR K=1 TO N
140   PRINT"Enter the constant term for eq. ";K:INPUT B(K)
150   FOR J=1 TO N
160     PRINT"Enter coefficient eq ";K;" variable ";J;INPUT A(K,J)
170 NEXT J,K
180 PRINT"Enter convergence criteria (default is";CR;")":INPUT CR
190 PRINT"Maximum number of iterations (default is";IM;")" :INPUT IM
200 REM
210 REM         Determine Pivotal Rows
220 REM
230 PRINT"Determining Pivots . . ."
240 FOR K=1 TO N:L(K)=K:S(K)=0
250   FOR J=1 TO N
```

```
260      S(K)=FN MAX(S(K),ABS(A(K,J)))
270 NEXT J,K
280 FOR K=1 TO N-1
290    RM=0
300    FOR I=K TO N
310      R=ABS(A(L(I),K)/S(L(I)))
320      IF R>RM THEN J=I:RM=R
330    NEXT I
340    REM Switch indicies
350    LK=L(J):L(J)= L(K):L(K)=LK
360 NEXT K
370 PRINT"1. Enter initial estimate, or 2. use b(i)/a(i,i)"
380 INPUT Z
390 IF Z=2 THEN 470 ELSE IF Z<>1 THEN 370
400 REM
410 REM user inputs estimate
420 REM
430 FOR K=1 TO N
440    PRINT"Enter estimate of x";K:INPUT X(K)
450 NEXT K:GOTO 540
460 REM use a(l(k),k)/b(1(k)) as long as b(1(k))<>0
470 FOR K=1 TO N
480 TF A(L(K),K) <> 0 Then X(K)=B(L(K))/A(L(K),K) ELSE X(K)=0
490    PRINT "Initial estimate of x(";K;")=";:PRINT USING U$;X(K)
500 NEXT K
510 REM
520 REM Determine result of convergence test
530 REM
540 TST=0:PRINT"Performing convergence test"
550 FOR K=1 TO N
560    SUM=0
570    FOR J=1 TO N
580      IF K=J THEN 600
590      SUM = SUM + ABS(A(L(K),J))
600    NEXT J
610    IF ABS(A(L(K),K))<=SUM THEN TST=-1
620 NEXT K
630 IF TST=0 THEN PRINT"Passed convergence test" ELSE PRINT"Failed
    convergence test"
640 REM
650 REM          Main Iteration Loop
660 REM
670 R=0:FOR K=1 TO N:SUM=0
680    FOR J=1 TO N
690      IF J=K THEN 710
700      SUM=SUM+A(L(K),J)*X(J)
710    NEXT J
720    X=(B(L(K))-SUM)/A(L(K),K)
730    REM Choose maximum for convergence test
740    R=FN MAX(ABS(X-X(K)),R)
```

```
750   X(K)=X
760     PRINT "x(";K;")=";:PRINT USING U$;X(K),
770 NEXT K:PRINT
780 PRINT"R=";R
790 IT=IT+1:PRINT"Iteration number . . .";IT
800 REM
810 REM        Now test convergence
820 REM
830 EN=FN DN(R,CR)
840 REM      If not done or past max iterations, then quit
850 IF EN THEN PRINT "Converged!":GOTO880
860 IF (IT<IM) THEN GOTO 670
870 PRINT"Did not converge!"
880 PRINT"Required ";IT;" iterations"
890 REM
900 REM          how much are we off?
910 REM
920 PRINT"Residuals by substitution"
930 FOR I=1 TO N:SUM=0
940    FOR J=1 TO N
950      SUM=SUM+A (I,J)*X(J)
960    NEXT J:PRINT "eq";I;" =";ABS(B(I)-SUM)
970 NEXT I
980 END
```

USING SEIDEL

You can easily substitute in your favorite system of simultaneous
equations for testing the system. First, you are asked for the number of
equations. Then, for each equation, you are asked for the value of the
constant term, and then the coefficients for the xs in the equation. You
are asked for the convergence criteria and the number of iterations
allowed. The convergence criteria is used to determine when we
have stopped converging. When the largest difference in estimations
is less than the convergence criteria, the program assumes convergence. The maximum number of iterations is the most iterations
allowed. Both of these variables have default values.

SEIDEL then computes the pivotal elements in a manner similar to
the one we used in the Gauss-Jordan elimination method. The index
array $L(i)$ stores the pivotal elements' indices. You are then asked
whether you wish to enter your own estimates or have the program
assume diagonal dominance and use b_i/a_{ii} for the estimate. After
these values are estimated, the program performs the diagonal dominance convergence test and reports the results. The program will attempt to solve the system regardless of the outcome of this test.

The main iteration loop is performed just as we have outlined. The program states whether it converged when it finishes, displays the number of iterations, and computes the residuals. To compute the residuals it substitutes the computed values into the original equations. This value is subtracted from the constant term, and the absolute value is taken. This is a measure of how good the estimates are. The residuals should be close to zero, if the estimates converged to the correct answer.

The Gauss-Seidel method is good for many applications. Perhaps surprisingly, it is fairly independent of the accuracy of the initial estimate. It is the method of choice for large matrices, particularly "band" systems, in which most of the off-diagonal elements are zero or close to zero in value. This is because of the severe roundoff errors that can occur when using the Gaussian methods on large, sparse, or ill-conditioned matrices. Band matrices come up in many applications, such as discretization of boundary value problems (a method of solving partial differential equations, which is not dealt with in this book).

Very large matrices often occur in the solution of partial differential equations, and with a system of 10,000 unknowns and as many equations, Gaussian methods are too slow (they would literally take years to solve on the largest computers) and accumulated roundoff error would make the results meaningless.

CHAPTER 5

Digital Approximation

An important topic in numerical analysis is the approximation of functions. Microcomputers ultimately know only the most elementary operations, such as addition and subtraction. Some of the new generation microprocessors have a hardware multiply and divide, but, generally, more advanced arithmetic operations must be performed in software. It is not bad enough that the computer cannot multiply directly, what must we do about the transcendental functions, such as sin x and exp (x)?

This section will not deal with the machine language routines necessary to implement arithmetic operations. Rather, we will discuss the problems of using a high-level language (BASIC) to find approximations for more complex functions, such as the transcendental functions.

APPROXIMATING ROOTS OF NUMBERS

There is a class of irrational functions that we can solve iteratively, finding roots of numbers. The nth root of a number can be written

$$f(x) = x^n - a = 0 \qquad (5\text{-}1)$$

where a is the number from which we will extract the nth root and x is the number that makes the equation true (therefore, it must be the nth root of a). We already know an easy method for solving this problem—the Newton-Raphson iteration. The Newton-Raphson iteration applied to this problem gives the iterative equation

$$x_{i+1} = x_i - \frac{f(x_i)}{f'(x_i)} \qquad (5\text{-}2)$$

Substituting in for $f(x)$ and $f'(x)$, we get

$$x_{i+1} = x_i - \frac{x^n - a}{nx^{n-1}} \qquad (5\text{-}3)$$

by using the equation $dx^n/dx = nx^{n-1}$.

Of course, if we want to get double-precision accuracy even though the x^y feature found in BASIC is single precision, we must avoid using the feature. If this feature was sufficiently accurate we wouldn't even need to use an iterative method to solve the problem. That's why we are restricting this example to integer roots. It will be easy to multiply out the xs in a FOR-NEXT loop to get x^n, when n is an integer. We use a peculiarity about the Newton-Raphson iteration. If there are n repeated roots (which we know by definition of the nth root) then convergence of the algorithm can be speeded up by applying the formula

$$x_{i+1} = x_i - \frac{nf(x)}{f'(x)} \qquad (5\text{-}4)$$

or

$$x_{i+1} = x_i - \frac{n(x^n - a)}{nx^{n-1}} \qquad (5\text{-}5)$$

Therefore

$$x_{i+1} = x_i - \frac{x^n - a}{x^{n-1}} \qquad (5\text{-}6)$$

Program 5-1 uses this relation.

Program 5-1. Roots of Numbers

```
10 REM      ROOTS, Newton style
20 REM define a,c,x as double precision; i,j as integers
30 DEFDBL A,C,X:DEFINT I,J,N
40 INPUT"Enter the base of the root";A
50 INPUT"Enter the root (2 for square root, 3 for cube root, etc)";N
60 INPUT"Initial guess of the answer";X
70 INPUT"Maximum number of iterations";IM
80 INPUT"Convergence criterion";CR
90 REM 2,4,6,8, who do we iterate??
100 FOR IT= 1 TO IM
110    X1=1
120    FOR I=1 TO N-1
130       X1=X1*X
```

```
140   NEXT I
150   X2=X1*X
160   REM x1 for f'(x), x2 for numerator
170   X=X-(X2-A)/X1
180   REM determine if met` criterion
190   X1=1
200   For I=1 TO N
210      X1=X1*X
220   NEXT I
230   IF ABS(X1-A) <=CR THEN PRINT"CONVERGED":GOTO 260
240 NEXT IT
250 PRINT"DID NOT CONVERGE"
260 PRINT "resulting value is";X
270 PRINT "X to the nth is   ";X1
280 PRINT "residual is       "; ABS(X1-A)
290 END
```

Although this is a simple example, it does provide a straightforward way to compute the nth root of a number to the maximal accuracy of your compiler or interpreter. Most BASICs have the transcendental functions in single precision only, but basic arithmetic is available in double precision. This allows the computation of the nth root of a number in double precision.

APPROXIMATING FUNCTIONS

The standard way to approximate more complicated functions, such as the transcendental functions, is to use a *Taylor series*. A Taylor series is an infinite series expansion of a function around some point. If the series converges to the true value of the function at that point, it is called *analytic* at that point. For a Taylor series to be applicable, the function must be infinitely differentiable, meaning that all derivatives exist (even though they may be identically zero) at the point in question. The definition of a Taylor series of $f(x)$ is given by

$$f(x) = f(a) + hf'(a) + \frac{h^2}{2} f''(a) + \ldots + \frac{h^n}{n!} f^{(n)}(a) + \ldots \qquad (5\text{-}7)$$

where $h=x-a$. The series is really most useful when you know the value of the function at some point a and wish to find it somewhere close by, at point x. The distance between x and a is, of course, $x-a$. If you write the Taylor series around the point $a=0$, then

$$f(x) = f(0) + xf'(0) + \frac{x^2}{2} f''(0) + \ldots + \frac{x^n}{n!} f^{(n)}(0) + \ldots \qquad (5\text{-}8)$$

is a special form called the *Maclaurin series*.

The Maclaurin series is the most commonly used form of the Taylor series. We know the values at $x=0$ for many functions, such as

$$\sin 0 \qquad = 0$$

$$\cos 0 \qquad = 1$$

$$\exp (0) \qquad = 1$$

$$\tan 0 \qquad = 0$$

$$\exp (\sin 0) \qquad = 1$$

Thus we can generate some infinite series:

$$\sin x = \sin 0 + x \cos 0 - \frac{x^2 \sin 0}{2!} - \frac{x^3 \cos 0}{3!}$$

$$= x - x^3 + x^5 - \ldots \tag{5-9}$$

$$\cos x = \cos 0 - x \sin 0 - \frac{x^2 \cos 0}{2!} + \frac{x^3 \sin 0}{3!} + \ldots$$

$$= 1 - \frac{x^2}{2!} + \frac{x^4}{4!} - \ldots \tag{5-10}$$

$$\exp (x) = \exp (0) + x \exp (0) + \frac{x^2 \exp (0)}{2!} + \frac{x^3 \exp (0)}{3!} + \ldots$$

$$= 1 + x + \frac{x^2}{2!} + \frac{x^3}{3!} + \frac{x^4}{4!} + \ldots \tag{5-11}$$

Of course, since we are in digital computing, we don't use all of the terms of the infinite series. We truncate the series, which will, we hope, not add too much error. The error depends on how many terms we use and the nature of the function around the point of evaluation.

Since we truncate the series, we must have some idea about when we have enough terms for the desired accuracy. A good general rule for convergence to a determined level, ϵ, is

$$| f_n(x) - f_{n+1}(x) | < \epsilon$$

This means that when the difference between two consecutive terms is less than some predetermined constant, then we can say we are there. One must be careful about using this in all circumstances. When each term gets much smaller in every term after the truncation, say by a factor of 10 or more, and the terms alternate in sign, this will be pretty good. In other situations, it will not be so good. Consider the series generated by

$$S = \sum_{i=1}^{\infty} \frac{1}{i}$$

You can always truncate this series with any ϵ, no matter how small, since the terms do get smaller and smaller. This series, however, is *divergent,* meaning that this infinite sum adds up to the value of infinity. There is no upper limit on this series. Therefore, you can see by this somewhat extreme example, that just because a series meets this convergence criterion, it does not mean that it really did converge.

In terms of evaluating the truncated series, since the series converges, it means that the terms get smaller and smaller. In what order should the terms be added together?

Since you diligently studied the first chapter on error analysis, you know that the smallest terms should be added together first, gradually adding the larger terms. This is to minimize the case of adding a small number to a large number. As you know from Chapter 1, this is a primary source of numerical error. As much as possible, the terms being added together should be as close in value as possible. For this reason the Taylor series should be evaluated in reverse (high-order terms to low-order term) to avoid serious truncation error.

Also, if your BASIC has the x^n function in single precision, but you need greater than single precision (as occurs with the TRS-80, as well as many other microcomputers), you should avoid using these less precise functions. Program 5-2 evaluates the Taylor series for exp(x) in double precision.

Program 5-2. Calculating exp (x) in Double Precision

```
10 REM EXP    in double precision
20 DEFDBL E,X:DEFINT I,J
30 INPUT"Enter exponent for e to the x";X
40 DIM E(10)
50 J=1:E(0)=1
60 FOR I=1 TO 10
70    E(I)=X*E(I−1)/J
80    J=J*I: REM J is factorial(i)
90 NEXT I
100 REM    Now evaluate in reverse order
110 FOR I=10 TO 0 STEP −1
120    EX=EX+E(I)
130 NEXT I
140 PRINT"result is ";ex
150 END
```

Program 5-2 calculates each of the ten terms in the truncated Taylor series for exp (x) and stores each element in an array. It is calculated in this way because each term can be easily calculated from the preceding terms. A definition used in this way is called a *recursive* definition, because each term is used to define later terms. Once all the terms are calculated, they are added together in the reverse order to minimize roundoff error.

Often, the Taylor series is analytic only within a small area around the point of evaluation, and this puts constraints on the values of x for which the Taylor series may be used. The Taylor series expansion for tan x around x=0, for example, is accurate only as long as x is between $-\pi/2$ and $\pi/2$ (radians, of course). Values outside this range must use angle reduction formulas to reduce the angle to be within this range. The same is true for sec x. The angle reduction approach takes advantage of the fact that these functions are periodic, meaning that they repeat. The period of the tangent function is π. Therefore tan x = tan (x + π). The tangent function is also an "odd" function, meaning that tan $(-x) = - $ tan x. These simple rules may be used in subroutines to reduce the angle to the appropriate range. If you use an approximation for log x that is only accurate within a specific range, you can take advantage of the fact that log ab = log a + log b, so that a and b are in the range, or at least can be further factored so that the approximation can be applied to arguments that are within the range of accuracy of the algorithm.

Even though the Taylor series converges to the correct value, we know nothing about how quickly it gets there. If the convergence is slow, then many terms may be necessary to obtain the desired accuracy. If the series converges quickly, then relatively few terms will be necessary. For Taylor series approximations, merely truncating the Taylor series is not an optimal way to use the Taylor series approach. Since the series will converge at infinity, it will necessarily be off by some amount if you truncate the series. You can, however, find more optimal coefficients for a truncated Taylor series-type approximation and get a better approximation with a truncated series. There are several sources that have some of these routines, Abramowitz and Stegun's *Handbook of Mathematical Functions* (Dover publications, 1972) is an excellent source. Dr. Ruckdeschel's *Basic Scientific Subroutines,* Volumes I and II (Byte Books, 1981), are another good source, complete with routines coded in Microsoft and North Star BASIC. Another good standard reference is Hastings' *Approximations for Digital Computers* (Princeton University Press, 1955). All these references provide many algorithms for approximations of common functions, with different degrees of accuracy and ranges for acceptable arguments. Since fewer terms are necessary with optimal coefficients, the optimal algorithms are faster for a given accuracy than the garden-variety Taylor series.

SOME APPROXIMATIONS OF FUNCTIONS

We will be presenting a few of the algorithms available from these sources, and they will be coded into the BASIC program SUBPACK. Each routine is commented, including the entry and exiting points, the values expected, etc. Since we are assuming that great accuracy is required, we will be presenting primarily algorithms that provide greater than single-precision accuracy. The algorithms presented in SUBPACK are given in Chart 5-1.

Many routines are useful only over a specific range. If you need to use the routine outside the range provided by the algorithm, you might try performing a transformation on the range of the algorithm. For example, routines that are accurate only within the range $-1 \le x \le 1$ can be changed to the range of $0 \le z < \infty$ by replacing x with z, where $z = (1-x)/(1+x)$. As x ranges from -1 to 1, z ranges from infinity to zero, making this a simple transformation for extending the useful range of the approximation. This transformation may be applied to the arctangent approximations.

These routines are nice, but it would be nice to be able to generate your own optimal approximations than have to rely on someone else's. After all, they may have different accuracy and argument range requirements than you. The creation of optimal approximations is more of an art than a science. There are many methods for generating useful approximations. We will deal with only a few here, including obtaining optimal coefficients for polynomials from least squares regression, interpolating polynomials, and spline interpolation. Of course, we have already discussed the ever popular Taylor series.

OPTIMAL COEFFICIENTS WITH LEAST SQUARES REGRESSION

We will discuss the topic of least squares regression briefly here and use the technique to derive more optimal coefficients for truncated series approximations of functions. Basically, least squares regression means that you are finding the line that "best fits" the data in the least squares sense. For a given line that goes "through" a group

Chart 5-1. Algorithms of Common Functions

1. arctan x

Function   arctan x
Range

$$-1 \leq x \leq 1$$

Approximation

$$\arctan x \approx \sum_{i=0}^{6} a_{2i+1} x^{2i+1}$$

Coefficients

$a_1 = 0.999\ 996\ 115$ $a_9 = 0.079\ 626\ 318$
$a_3 = -0.333\ 173\ 758$ $a_{11} = -0.033\ 606\ 269$
$a_5 = 0.198\ 078\ 690$ $a_{13} = 0.006\ 812\ 411$
$a_7 = -0.132335096$

Accuracy

$$\pm\ 2 \times 10^{-7}$$

Reference
Approximations for Digital Computers
by C. Hastings Jr.,
Princeton University Press, 1955

2. arctan x

Function   arctan x
Range $0 \leq x < \infty$

$$\arctan x = \pi/4 + \sum_{i=0}^{6} a_{2i+1} \left[(x-1)/(x+1)\right]^{2i+1}$$

Coefficients

(same as for approximation 1)

Accuracy   (same as for approximation 1)
Reference
Approximations for Digital Computers
by C. Hastings Jr.,
Princeton University Press, 1955

Chart 5-1-cont. Algorithms of Common Functions

3. cos x

Function   cos x

Range

$$0 \leq x \leq \pi/2$$

Approximation

$$\cos x = 1 + a_2x^2 + a_4x^4 + a_6x^6 + a_8x^8 + a_{10}x^{10}$$

Coefficients

$a_2 = -0.499\ 999\ 996\ 3$ $a_8 = 0.000\ 024\ 760\ 9$

$a_4 = 0.041\ 666\ 641\ 8$ $a_{10} = -0.000\ 000\ 260\ 5$

$a_6 = -0.001\ 388\ 839\ 7$

Accuracy

$$\pm\ 2 \times 10^{-9}$$

Reference

Rational Approximations of Functions
by B. Carlson and M. Goldstein,
Los Almos Scientific Laboratory LA-1943, 1955

4. sin x

Function   sin x

Range

$$0 \leq x \leq \pi/2$$

Approximation

$$\sin x = x(1 + a_2x^2 + a_4x^4 + a_6x^6 + a_8x^8 + a_{10}x^{10})$$

Coefficients

$a_2 = -0.499\ 999\ 996\ 3$ $a_8 = 0.000\ 002\ 752\ 6$

$a_4 = 0.041\ 666\ 641\ 8$ $a_{10} = -0.000\ 000\ 023\ 9$

$a_6 = -0.001\ 388\ 839\ 7$

Accuracy

$$\pm\ 2 \times 10^{-9}$$

Reference

Rational Approximations of Functions
by B. Carlson and M. Goldstein,
Los Almos Scientific Laboratory LA-1943, 1955

cont. on next page

Chart 5-1-cont. Algorithms of Common Functions

5. exp (−x)

Function $\qquad e^{-x}$

Range
$$0 \le x < \infty$$

Approximation
$$\exp(-x) = (1 + a_1x + a_2x^2 + a_3x^3 + a_4x^4)^{-4}$$

Coefficients

$a_1 = 0.249\ 910\ 35$ $\qquad$ $a_3 = 0.002\ 277\ 23$

$a_2 = 0.031\ 585\ 65$ $\qquad$ $a_4 = 0.000\ 266\ 95$

Accuracy
$$\pm 2 \times 10^{-5}$$

Reference

Approximations for Digital Computers
by C. Hastings Jr.,
Princeton University Press, 1955

6. exp (−x)

Function $\qquad e^{-x}$

Range
$$0 \le x < \infty$$

Approximation
$$\exp(-x) = (1 + a_1x + a_2x^2 + a_3x^3 + a_4x^4 + a_5x^5 + a_6x^6)^{-4}$$

Coefficients

$a_1 = 0.249\ 998\ 684\ 2$ $\qquad$ $a_4 = 0.000\ 171\ 562\ 0$

$a_2 = 0.031\ 257\ 583\ 2$ $\qquad$ $a_5 = 0.000\ 005\ 430\ 2$

$a_3 = 0.002\ 591\ 371\ 2$ $\qquad$ $a_6 = 0.000\ 000\ 690\ 6$

Accuracy
$$\pm 2 \times 10^{-7}$$

Reference

Approximations for Digital Computers
by C. Hastings Jr.,
Princeton University Press, 1955.

of data points, the distance between the line (the value of the point as estimated by the line) and the point itself is a measure of the extent to which the line fits the data. If all the points lie right on the line, then the line estimates the data extremely well. Anytime you need to calculate a point from this group of data, you can use the line to estimate it.

If the distance between the line and the point is large, then the line is not a good estimator of the data set. The larger the difference, the less well the line estimates the points. If we take this distance between the nearest point on the line and the data point and square it, we have a measure of the distance that is always positive. If we then add up all these differences between each of the points and the line, we get a sum of squared distances. Note that if we did not square the number, some of these distances would be negative, canceling out the effect of the positive distances. By using the distance squared, we avoid this problem, and have a much better measure of the "fit" of the line to the data.

The goal of least squares is to find the line that minimizes the sum of distances squared, hence the name "least squares." Linear regression is usually done with least squares, but a line may not be the best fit. If the data is actually describing a parabola or some other nonlinear shape, then it will be difficult to fit a line to the data. Since the data is intrinsically nonlinear, then using a line, even the best line, will not provide very good estimation of the data set. We may also use regression techniques to fit curvilinear (curves, not straight lines) structures to data with essentially the same technique. You are still trying to find the best curve to fit the data. A common class of curvilinear regression is the fitting of polynomials to data. Since our Taylor series is, after all, a polynomial, curvilinear regression provides a simple technique for finding the coefficients that make a given polynomial best fit the data.

There are many sources of high-accuracy data for a number of irrational and transcendental functions. One of the best is *Handbook of Mathematical Functions* by Abramowitz and Stegun. Using a large number of data points and a suitable polynomial, you can find better coefficients for a truncated Taylor series than those provided by the Taylor series.

The approximations in Chart 5-2 were constructed in this manner by Dr. F. R. Ruckdeschel and published in his fine book, *Basic Scientific Subroutines*, Volume I (Byte Books, 1981). He has kindly given permission to reprint them here.

Chart 5-2. Common Functions by Least Squares Regression

1. sin x

Function   sin x

Range

$$-\pi/2 \le x \le \pi/2$$

Approximation

$$\sin x \approx x + a_1 x^3 + a_2 x^5 + a_3 x^7 + a_4 x^9 + a_5 x^{11} + a_6 x^{13}$$

Coefficients

$a_1 = -0.166\ 666\ 666\ 667\ 133\ 4$
$a_2 = 0.008\ 333\ 333\ 338\ 090\ 67$
$a_3 = -0.000\ 198\ 412\ 715\ 551\ 283$
$a_4 = 0.000\ 002\ 755\ 758\ 975\ 076\ 2$
$a_5 = -0.000\ 000\ 025\ 070\ 598\ 762\ 07$
$a_6 = 0.000\ 000\ 000\ 164\ 105\ 986\ 683$

Accuracy

$$10^{-14}$$

Reference

Basic Scientific Subroutines, Volume I,
by F. R. Ruckdeshel, Byte Books 1981

2. cos x

Function   cos x

Range

$$-\pi/2 \le x \le \pi/2$$

Approximation

$$\cos x \approx x + a_1 x^2 + a_2 x^4 + a_3 x^6 + a_4 x^8 + a_5 x^{10} + a_6 x^{12}$$

Coefficients

$a_1 = -0.499\ 999\ 999\ 998\ 2$
$a_2 = 0.041\ 666\ 666\ 646\ 51$
$a_3 = -0.001\ 388\ 888\ 805\ 755$
$a_4 = 0.000\ 024\ 801\ 428\ 034$
$a_5 = -0.000\ 000\ 275\ 421\ 332\ 4$
$a_6 = 0.000\ 000\ 002\ 018\ 940\ 5$

Accuracy

$$10^{-12}$$

Reference

Basic Scientific Subroutines, Volume I,
by F. R. Ruckdeshel, Byte Books 1981

Chart 5-2-cont. Common Functions by Least Squares Regression

3. ln x

Function   ln x

Range

$$1 \leq x \leq e$$

Approximation

$$\ln x \approx 1 + \sum_{i=1}^{9} a_i z^{2i+1}$$

where

$$z = (x-c)/(x+c) \qquad c = 1.648\ 721\ 270\ 7$$

Coefficients

$a_0 = 2.000\ 000\ 000\ 00$
$a_1 = 0.666\ 666\ 724\ 43$
$a_2 = 0.399\ 989\ 528\ 8$
$a_3 = 0.286\ 436\ 047$
$a_4 = 0.197\ 959\ 107$
$a_5 = 0.628\ 353\ 3$
$a_6 = -4.546\ 92$
$a_7 = 28.117$
$a_8 = -86.42$
$a_9 = 106.1$

Accuracy

$$10^{-14}$$

Reference
Basic Scientific Subroutines, Volume I,
by F. R. Ruckdeshel, Byte Books 1981

These routines are also coded into the Program 5-3, SUBPACK. They may be linked in with your programs that require them.

Program 5-3. SUBPACK Function Subroutine Package

```
10 REM   SUBPACK: INITIALIZE SUBROUTINE PACKAGE AT 9000
20 REM   PUT YOUR PROGRAM IN LINES 50-8999
30 REM   AVOID PUTTING ANY DATA STATEMENTS BEFORE 9000
40 REM   UNLESS YOU READ THEM BEFORE CALLING 9000
50 PRINT"INITIALIZING . . .":GOSUB 9000:REM TEST SUBROUTINES
60 PRINT"ENTER THE NUMBER OF THE SUBROUTINE:"
70 PRINT"1. ARCTAN(X)      5. EXP(X)"
80 PRINT"2. ARCTAN(X)      6. EXP(X)"
```

```
90 PRINT"3. COS(X)          7.SIN(X)"
100 PRINT"4. SIN(X)          8. COS(X)"
110 PRINT"          9. LN(X)"
120 INPUT J
130 INPUT"ENTER THE VALUE OF X";X
135 REM ROUTINE 1. 2. 3. 4. 5. 6. 7. 8. 9.
140 ON J GOSUB 9440, 9460, 9550, 9620, 9680, 9750, 9820, 9880, 9940
150 PRINT"THE ANSWER IS ";AN
160 REM
180 REM   AGAIN OR NOT
190 INPUT"1.   AGAIN      2. QUIT";J1
200 IF J1=2 THEN END ELSE GOTO 60
9000 DEFINT I,J:DEFDBL A,X:AP=VAL ("3.141592654"):DIM X(20)
9010 XC=VAL("1.6487212707")
9020 DATA "0.999996115", "−.3317759", "0.19807869", "−.12335096"
9030 DATA "0.079626318", "−.0333606269", "0.006812411"
9040 REM   READ IN COEFFICIENTS FOR ROUTINES 1 AND 2 (ARCTAN)
9050 DIM A1(7)
9060 FOR I=1 TO 7:READ A$:A1(I)=VAL(A$):NEXT I
9070 DATA "−.4999999963", "0.0416666418", "−.00133888397",
     "0.0000247609", "−.0000002605"
9080 REM   READ IN COEFFICIENTS FOR ROUTINE 3 (COS)
9090 DIM A3(5)
9100 FOR I=1 TO 5:READ A$:A3(I)=VAL(A$):NEXT I
9110 DATA "−.1666666664", "0.008333315", "−.000198409",
     "0.0000027526", "−.0000000239"
9120 REM   READ IN COEFFICIENTS FOR ROUTINE 4 (SIN)
9130 DIM A4(5)
9140 FOR I=1 TO 5:READ A$:A4(I)=VAL(A$):NEXT I
9150 DATA "0.24991035", "0.03158565", "0.00227723", "0.00026695"
9160 REM   READ IN COEFFICIENTS FOR ROUTINE 5 (EXP)
9170 DIM A5(4)
9180 FOR I=1 TO 4:READ A$:A5(I)=VAL(A$):NEXT I
9190 DATA "0.2499986842", "0.0312575832", "0.0025913712", "0.000171562"
9200 DATA "0.0000054302", "0.0000006906"
9210 REM   READ IN COEFFICIENTS FOR ROUTINE 6 (EXP)
9220 DIM A6(6)
9230 FOR I=1 TO 6:READ A$:A6(I)=VAL(A$):NEXT I
9240 DATA "−.1666666666671334", "0.00833333333809067",
     "−.000198412715551283"
9250 DATA "0.0000027557589750762", "−.00000002507029876207",
     "0.000000000164105986683"
9260 REM   READ IN COEFFICIENTS FOR ROUTINE 7 (SIN)
9270 DIM A7(6)
9280 FOR I=1 TO 6:READ A$:A7(I)=VAL(A$):NEXT I
9290 DATA "−.4999999999982", "0.04166666664651", "−.001388888805755"
9300 DATA "0.000024801428034", "−.0000002754213324",
     "0.0000000020189405"
9310 REM   READ IN COEFFICIENTS FOR ROUTINE 8 (COS)
9320 DIM A8(6)
```

```
9330 FOR I=1 TO 6:READ A$:A8(I)=VAL(A$):NEXT I
9340 DATA "2.0", "0.66666672443", "0.3999895288", "0.286436047"
9350 DATA "0.197959107", "0.6283533", "-4.54692", "28.117", "-86.42",
     "106.1"
9360 REM    READ IN COEFFICIENTS FOR ROUTINE 9 (LOG)
9370 DIM A9(10)
9380 FOR I=1 TO 10:READ A$:A9(I)=VAL(A$):NEXT I
9400 REM    APPROXIMATION #1: ARCTAN(X); -1<=X <=1
9410 REM    ACCURACY:   2 E-7
9420 REM    ADAPTED FROM C. HASTINGS (SEE REFERENCES)
9430 REM    PASS X AS ARGUMENT
9440 F1=0:GOTO 9470
9450 REM    ENTRY POINT FOR APPROXIMATION 2: ARCTAN(X) 0<=X
     <INFINITY
9460 X=(X-1)/ (X+1):F1=1
9470 AR=0:X1=X:FOR I=1 TO 7:X(I)=X1:X1=X1 *X*X*X:NEXT I
9480 FOR I=7 TO 1 STEP -1:AR=AR+A1(I) *X(I)
9490 NEXT I
9500 AN=AR+AP/4*F1
9510 RETURN:REM    AN RETURNS VALUE
9520 REM    APPROXIMATION #3: COS(X); 0<=X<= PI/2
9530 REM    ACCURACY:   2 E-9
9540 REM    ADAPTED FROM CARLSON AND GOLDSTEIN (SEE REFER-
ENCES)
9550 AC=0:X1=X *X:FOR I=1 TO 5:X(I)=X1:X1= X1*X*X:NEXT I
9560 FOR I=5 TO 1 STEP -1:AC=AC +A3(I)*X(I)
9570 NEXT I
9580 AN=AC+1:RETURN:REM    AN RETURNS VALUE
9590 REM    APPROXIMATION #4: SIN(X); 0<=X <=PI/2
9600 REM    ACCURACY:   2 E-9
9610 REM    ADAPTED FROM CARLSON AND GOLDSTEIN (SEE REFER-
     ENCES)
9620 AC=0:X1=X*X:FOR I=1 TO 5:X(I)=X1:X1=X1 *X*X:NEXT I
9630 FOR I=5 TO 1 STEP -1:AC=AC+A4(I) *X(I)
9640 NEXT I:AN=(AC+1) *X:RETURN
9650 REM    APPROXIMATION #5:   EXP(X);   0<=X<INFINITY
9660 REM    ACCURACY:   2 E-5
9670 REM    ADAPTED FROM CARLSON AND GOLDSTEIN (SEE REFER-
     ENCES)
9680 AE=0:X1=X:FOR I=1 TO 4:X(I)=X1:XI=X1* X:NEXT I
9690 FOR I=4 TO 1 STEP -1:AE=AE+A5 (I)*X(I):NEXT I:AE=AE+1
9700 AN=1/AE/AE/AE/AE
9710 RETURN:REM    AN RETURNS VALUE
9720 REM    APPROXIMATION #6: EXP(X): 0<=X<INFINITY
9730 REM    ACCURACY:   2 E-5
9740 REM    ADAPTED FROM CARLSON AND GOLDSTEIN (SEE REFER-
     ENCES)
9750 AE=0:X1=X:FOR I=1 TO 6:X(I)=X1: X1=X1*X:NEXT I
9760 FOR I=6 TO 1 STEP -1:AE=AE+A6(I) *X(I):NEXT I:AE=AE+1
9770 AN=1/AE/AE/AE/AE
```

```
9780 RETURN
9790 REM    APPROXIMATION #7: SIN(X); -PI/2<=X <=PI/2
9800 REM    ACCURACY:   1 E-14
9810 REM    ADAPTED FROM RUCKDESCHEL (SEE REFERENCES)
9820 AS=0:X1=X:FOR I=1 TO 6:X(I)=X1:X1=X1 *X*X: NEXT I
9830 FOR I=6 TO 1 STEP -1:AS=AS+A7(I) *X(I)
9840 NEXT I:AN=AS:RETURN: REM    AN RETURNS VALUE
9850 REM    APPROXIMATION #8: COS(X); - PI/2<=X <=PI/2
9860 REM    ACCURACY: 1 E-12
9870 REM    ADAPTED FROM RUCKDESCHEL
9880 AC=0:X1= X*X:FOR I=1 TO 6:X(I)=X1:X1= X1*X*X:NEXT I
9890 FOR I=6 TO 1 STEP -1:AC=AC+A8(I) *X(I):NEXT I
9900 AN=AC:RETURN:REM    AN RETURNS THE VALUE
9910 REM    APPROXIMATION #6: LN(X);   1<=X<= E
9920 REM    ACCURACY:   1 E=14
9930 REM    ADAPTED FROM RUCKDESCHEL
9940 AE=0:X1= (X-XC)/(X+XC):FOR I=1 TO 10 X(I)=X1:X1=X1 *X*X:NEXT I
9950 FOR I=10 TO 1 STEP -1:AE=AE+A6 (I)*X(I):NEXT I: AN=AE+1/2
9960 RETURN
```

INTERPOLATING POLYNOMIALS

The use of Taylor series and optimal least squares coefficients for truncated series is fine for many applications. Taylor series approximations can be poor for a number of reasons. The function may not be analytic in the region, which means that the series will not converge to the correct value (if it converges at all). For a number of functions, the Taylor series is very slowly converging. The Taylor series for the arctangent function is one of these. To obtain an accuracy of 10^{-7}, you must sum about 5×10^7 terms, making it useless for digital approximations. Even if you had the diligence to add up the necessary terms, roundoff error would make the result meaningless. Using optimal coefficients can greatly speed the convergence for truncated series.

Least squares regression will not fit the end points of your data very well. Further, as with all polynomial approximations, increasing the order of the fitting polynomial often decreases the accuracy of the estimation. Polynomials are highly oscillatory. Even if the data points that are known are exactly fit by the polynomial, intermediate values may be very poorly estimated by the polynomial. This particularly occurs when the fitted function is not very "smooth" and the order of the fitting polynomial is high.

In statistical analysis, one works with noisy data. The noise may be from a number of sources, including "shot noise" (predicted by quantum theory), inaccuracy of instrumentation, and so on. When you know the exact value of your function at discrete points, an interpolating polynomial can be used to fit the data. An interpolating polynomial is a polynomial that exactly fits the data and is used to fit a relatively small table of data. In general, to fit n points in this way, it will require a polynomial of order $n-1$. You can see why it is good to avoid large tables with this method. To fit 100 data points within a 99th-degree polynomial would be a very slow way to get your answers, and roundoff error would certainly appear in the results. Finally, high-order polynomials are highly oscillatory, meaning that a better overall fit may be obtained with other methods, such as least squares regression using a lower-order polynomial.

One of the more common interpolating polynomial is called Newton's interpolating polynomial (NIP). Suppose that we have a table of data such as is shown below.

x	x_1 x_2 x_3 x_4 x_5
y	y_1 y_2 y_3 y_4 y_5

Newton's polynomial is a polynomial that passes through each of the points in the table. Consider the case when you have a table of two points, (x_1, y_1) and (x_2, y_2). The polynomial that passes through both points is a simple straight line:

$$p(x) = y_1 + [(y_2 - y_1)/(x_2 - x_1)] (x - x_1) \qquad (5\text{-}12)$$

If you substitute x_1 and x_2 into this line, you will find that the results are y_1 and y_2, respectively. That is the condition placed on the polynomial—it must exactly present the values in the table. The values of the table are called the *nodes,* and the polynomial is said to *interpolate at the nodes.*

If you have a polynomial that produces some of the points in your data table and wish to add more, you can use a simple approach. If you have a polynomial $p(x)$ that does provide n of the points, e.g., $p(x_i)$ gives y_i, then the polynomial

$$q(x) = p(x) + a(x - x_1) (x - x_2) \ldots (x - x_n) \qquad (5\text{-}13)$$

also reproduces the n points since the second term will go to zero when x equals x_1 through x_n. We can now find the value of the multiplicative constant a so that $q(x_{n+1}) = y_{n+1}$. This method can be used to create a high-order polynomial that exactly reproduces the data points in a table.

Program 5-4, InterNewton, calculates the final coefficients of the nth-order Newton interpolating polynomial necessary to exactly reproduce the N points of a table. The x values are stored in a singly-dimensioned array $X(I)$, and the associated y values are stored in $Y(I)$. The values stored in $Y(I)$ are then changed into appropriate coefficients for the polynomial. In the second half of the program, you may interpolate using the polynomial by entering a value, x. The program then evaluates the polynomial and displays the results. You can make this more general purpose by writing simple routines to save the $Y(I)$ array after the polynomial coefficients are stored there. This means that you only have to calculate them once, but can recall them from disk and use them as needed.

Program 5-4. Newton Interpolation Polynomial

```
10 REM InterNewton—interpolating polynomial
20 INPUT "Enter number of points to be entered";N
30 PRINT "Enter x,y values"
40 FOR I=1 TO N
50    INPUT X(I),Y(I)
60 NEXT I
70 REM Make coefficients
80 FOR J=1 TO N-1
90    FOR I=1 TO N-J
100      Y(N-I+1) =(Y(N-I+1) -Y(N-I))/(X (N-I+1)-X(N- I-J+1))
110 NEXT J,I
120 REM Now interpolate
130 INPUT "Enter an x value to interpolate";X
140 E=Y(N)
150 FOR I=1 TO N-1
160    E=E(X-X(N-I)) +Y(N-I)
170 NEXT I
180 PRINT "Result is ";E
190 INPUT "Again (y/n)";A$
200 IF A$="Y" OR A$="y" THEN 130
210 END
```

SPLINE APPROXIMATIONS

There are many other approximations methods, such as Chebyshev polynomials and rational polynomial approximations, but a popular and widely used method is called *spline approximations*. A spline function is a function that is made up of many pieces that are fitted together with certain "smoothness" criteria. Each piece is a polynomial that is used over an interval. The pieces are connected at points called *nodes;* these nodes are the data points that are used to generate the spline function. A different piece is used depending on which interval of the spline function the interpolating value falls. The degree of the spline function refers to the order of the polynomial pieces used to approximate the function. A spline function of order 1 uses linear pieces on each interval, as shown in Fig. 5-1. A spline function of order 2 uses a second-order polynomial in each interval.

Fig. 5-1 shows intuitively what the spline function does. A different polynomial is used depending on which interval holds the value at which the function is to be evaluated. Linear approximations are useful, but one can see that at the nodes the approximation is not very smooth. This smoothness is intuitively evident by inspection of Fig. 5-1, and what it means mathematically is that there is a discontinuity in the first derivative of the function. When smoothness is required, higher-order spline functions are used, with the cubic spline being by far the most popular for a number of technical reasons, including the fact that odd-powered splines behave better than even-powered ones.

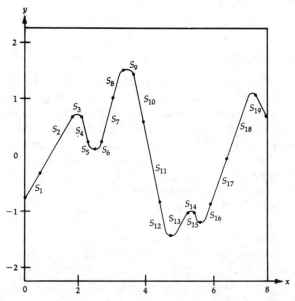

Fig. 5-1. Approximation by cubic splines.

For smoothness of the derivative of order k, the limit of the function approached from the right and left must be equal at the nodes. If we denote approaching a point a to the right as $x \to a^+$, and approaching a point a to the left to be $x \to a^-$, then this condition may be written

$$\lim_{x \to a^+} S^{(k)}(x) = \lim_{x \to a^-} S^{(k)}(x)$$

where $S^{(k)}(x)$ is the kth-order derivative of $S(x)$.

This is obviously not true of the first-order spline function, since the derivative of a line is a constant, and Fig. 5-1 shows the slopes of the lines of adjacent intervals are not the same. In creating cubic splines, we join a group of cubic polynomials so that the spline function is continuous in the first and second derivatives. From now on, we will consider only cubic spline functions.

If we have n data points that we wish to approximate with our piecewise spline function, then we construct a set of $n-1$ cubic polynomials. We must place conditions on the polynomials:

1. The spline function represents the data table exactly. That is $S(x_i) = x_i$, where (x_i, y_i) is a member of the data set giving rise to the spline function.
2. The spline function and its first two derivatives are continuous at the nodes, or

$$\lim_{x \to x_i -} S^{(k)}(x_i) = \lim_{x \to x_i +} S^{(k)}(x_i)$$

where x_i is any and all nodes, and $k = 0$, 1, or 2.

Two more conditions must be specified to use all the degrees of freedom available. Degrees of freedom, you may recall from elementary inferential statistics, is equal to the number of determined items minus the number of restrictions placed on the data. There are $n-1$ polynomials, each with four coefficients, for a total of $4(n-1)$ coefficients. There are also $4(n-1)-2$ restrictions placed on the data, since each polynomial must go through two known points ($2(n-1)$ conditions), the first and second derivatives for each must be continuous for each of the $n-2$ interior data points (another $2(n-2)$ conditions). We have two more free conditions left, or two more degrees of freedom. A common restriction is to force the second derivatives at the end points to be zero. The spline function resulting from this restriction is called a *natural spline*.

The coding involved in generating spline functions from a data table is simple, but close attention is required if you wish to fully understand what is going on. We will define the interval between two adjacent nodes to be $[x_i, x_{i+1}]$, where i stands for the ith data point from the table. We will fit a cubic polynomial, $S_i(x)$, to this interval. We know (because we demand it by definition) that the second derivative of each of these cubic polynomials $S_i''(x)$ is continuous. Since $S(x)$ is a cubic polynomial, then $S''(x)$ must be a linear polynomial and the second derivative at the end point for the polynomial $S_i(x)$, $S_i''(x_{i+1})$, must equal the second derivative of the next polynomial, $S_{i+1}(x)$, at the point x_{i+1}. This is another way of stating that the second derivatives are continuous at the nodes. They must have the same value whether it is the second derivative of the previous polynomial $S_i(x)$ evaluated at its ending node, or whether it is the second derivative of the current polynomial $S_{i+1}(x)$ evaluated at its beginning node. The value of the second derivative at x_i we will call a_i. We know that $a_0 = a_n = 0$, since we want a natural spline, as defined above.

Since $S''(x)$ is a linear polynomial that takes on the value a_i at x_i and the value a_{i+1} at x_{i+1}, we have two points that are distinct but both fall on the line defined by $S''(x)$. This uniquely defines the line $S''(x)$:

$$S_i''(x) = [a_{i+1}\ (x - x_1) + a_i\ (x_{i+1} - x)]\ /(x_{i+1} - x_i) \tag{5-15}$$

You will note that when $x = x_i$, then S'' gives a_i, and when $x = x_{i+1}$, then S'' gives a_{i+1}, which is what we wanted.

This is all well and good, but we don't want $S''(x)$; we want $S(x)$. We get $S(x)$ by integrating $S''(x)$ twice. This yields the rather imposing equation

$$S_i(x) = \frac{a_{i+1}}{6(x_{i+1} - x_i)}\ (x - x_i)^3 + \frac{a_i}{6(x_{i+1} - x_i)}\ (x_{i+1} - x)^3$$

$$+ b(x - x_i) + c(x_{i+1} - x) \tag{5-16}$$

where b and c are constants generated during the integration. These may be uniquely determined from the fact that we know $S_i(x_i) = y_i$ and $S_i(x_{i+1}) = y_{i+1}$.

If we let h_i be the size of the interval, that is,

$$h_i = x_{i+1} - x_i$$

then Equation 5-16 may be rewritten as Equation 5-17:

$$S_i(x) = \frac{a_{i+1}}{6h_i}\ (x - x_i)^3 + \frac{a_i}{6h_i}\ (x_{i+1} - x)^3 + \left(\frac{y_{i+1}}{h_i} - \frac{a_{i+1}h_i}{6} \right)\ (x - x_i)$$

$$+ \left(\frac{y_i}{h_i} - \frac{a_i h_i}{6} \right)\ (x_{i+1} - x) \tag{5-17}$$

There remains one more condition to be imposed on the spline function. The first derivative is also continuous. That is identical with the mathematical statement

$$S_i'(x_i) = S_{i+1}'(x_i) \tag{5-18}$$

By taking the derivatives of Equation 5-17 for both the ith and the $(i-1)$th interval and setting them equal to each other, you can derive Equation 5-19:

$$h_{i-1}a_{i-1} + 2(h_{i-1} + h_i) + h_i a_{i+1} = \frac{6(y_{i+1} - y_i)}{h_i} - \frac{6(y_i - y_{i-1})}{h_{i-1}} \quad (5\text{-}19)$$

Equation 5-19 is a sample equation from a system of $n-2$ such equations in which everything is known except the a_is. Since we are deriving a natural spline, we know that $a_0 = a_n = 0$. We can solve this system using methods we have already devised.

The matrix of coefficients that we have is called a *band system* or a *tridiagonal system* because most of the coefficients in any given equation are zero. In the *i*th equation, only a_{i-1}, a_i, and a_{i+1} occur, giving rise to an augmented matrix that looks like

$$\begin{pmatrix} d & u & 0 & 0 & 0 \\ l & d & u & 0 & 0 \\ 0 & l & d & u & 0 \\ 0 & 0 & l & d & u \\ 0 & 0 & 0 & l & d \end{pmatrix} \begin{pmatrix} a_1 \\ a_2 \\ a_3 \\ a_4 \\ a_5 \end{pmatrix} = \begin{pmatrix} b_1 \\ b_2 \\ b_3 \\ b_4 \\ b_5 \end{pmatrix}$$

It is called tridiagonal because the main diagonal coefficients appear (the *d*s), as well as the diagonal just above (supradiagonal) and below (subdiagonal) the main diagonal. All the other coefficients are zero. Since this is the case, we can shorten the general Gaussian elimination method used to solve the system of equations. A BASIC subroutine called Tri-Diag does this (Program 5-5).

Program 5-5. Tridiagonal System Solver

```
1000 REM Tri-Diag routine
1010 REM Solves a tridiagonal system of equations
1020 REM B(i) holds the constants of the equations
1030 REM D(i) holds the main diagonal coefficients
1040 REM L(i) holds the lower diagonal coefficients
1050 REM U(i) holds the upper diagonal coefficients
1060 REM N=number of equations to solve
1070 FOR I=2 TO N
1080    X=L(I-1)/D(I-1)
1090    D(I)=D(I)-X*U(I -1)
1100    B(I)=B(I)-X *B(I-1)
1110 NEXT I
1120 B(N)=B(N)/D(N)
1130 REM Now backwards substitution
1140 FOR I=1 TO N-1
1150    B(N-I) =(B(N-I) -U(N-I) *B(N-I+1)) /D(N-I)
1160 NEXT I
1170 REM Answers are stored in B(i)
1180 RETURN
```

The routine Tri-Diag takes some computational shortcuts allowed because we know *a priori* that all elements in the coefficient matrix not on the main diagonal or the adjacent lower or upper diagonals must be zero. We will use this routine in Program 5-6 to find the a_is to generate the spline function. In the case of the spline function with four table values, the tridiagonal system to be solved is

$$\begin{pmatrix} 2(h_1+h_2) & h_2 & 0 \\ h_2 & 2(h_2+h_3) & h_3 \\ 0 & h_3 & 3(h_3+h_4) \end{pmatrix} \begin{pmatrix} a_1 \\ a_2 \\ a_3 \end{pmatrix} = \begin{pmatrix} b_1 \\ b_2 \\ b_3 \end{pmatrix}$$

Program 5-6. Spline Function

```
10 REM Spline function generator
20 CLEAR 200:DEFINT I,J:DIM I
30 CLS:INPUT"Spline analysis: Number of table data points";N
40 DIM B(N),D(N),L(N),U(N),X(N),Y(N)
50 PRINT"Enter data points :"
60 FOR I=1 TO N
70   PRINT"X,Y for table entry #";I
80   INPUT X(I),Y(I)
90 NEXT I
100 PRINT"Data entry complete. Now calculating spline function."
110 REM
120 D(1)=1:U(1)=0: L(1)=0:B(1)=0
130 FOR I=2 TO N−1
140   D(I)=2* (X(I+1)−X(I−1))
150   U(I)=X(I+1) −X(I)
160   L(I)=U(I):REM since the matrix is symmetric
170   T=(Y(I+1) −Y(I))/U(I)
180   B(I)=6*(T− (Y(I)−Y(I−1))/(X(I) −X(I−1)))
190 NEXT I
200 D(N)=1:U(N−1) =0:L(N−1)=0:B(N) =0
210 REM solve symmetric tridiagonal system
220 GOSUB 420
230 REM now interpolate from spline function
240 INPUT"Enter a value to interpolate from";X
250 REM find which interval it is in (I=interval number)
260 FOR J=1 TO N−2
270   I=N−J
280   IF X−X(I) >=0 THEN T=X(I):GOTO 330
290 NEXT J
300 REM if it gets here, then X is in the first interval
310 I=1:T=X−X(1)
320 REM interpolate from spline in interval # i
330 H=X(I+1)− X(I)
340 A=T*(B (I+1)−B (I))/6/H + B(I)/2
350 B=T*A+ (Y(I+1)−Y (I))/H−H* (2*B(I) +B(I+1))/6
360 SP=T*B+Y(I)
370 REM Print result of interpolation
380 PRINT"The interpolated result is :";SP
```

```
390 INPUT"1. AGAIN      2. QUIT";Q
400 IF Q=1 THEN 240
410 END
420 REM TRI-DIAG ROUTINE
430 REM Solves a tridiagonal system of equations
440 REM B(I) holds the constants of the equations
450 REM D(I) holds the main diagonal coefficients
460 REM L(I) holds the lower diagonal coefficients
470 REM U(I) holds the upper diagonal coefficients
480 REM in this case, the matrix is symmetric,
490 REM ergo, U(I)=L(I)
500 REM N=Number of equations in system
510 FOR I=2 TO N
520    X=L(I-1)/D (I-1)
530    D(I)=D(I) -X*U(I-1)
540    B(I)=B(I) -X*B(I-1)
550 NEXT I
560 B(N)=B(N)/D(N)
570 REM now backwards substitution
580 FOR I=1 TO N-1
590    B(N-1)= (B(N-I)-U(N-I)*(N-I+1))/D(N-I)
600 NEXT I
610 REM Coefficients for spline function are stored in B(I)
620 RETURN
```

Program 5-6 generates a spline function approximation for a table of data points. The table of data points doesn't have to form a function in the mathematical sense; a data table that describes a spiral, for example, can have any number of values corresponding to $x=1$. However, since we use a distinct cubic polynomial to interpolate between data points in our table, we need only keep track of the interval the point is in to get a reasonable interpolation. The program also does not check to see if the value falls in the range of interpolated values. If you replace the data entry routine (lines 50–90) with the line

```
50 FOR I=1 TO N:X(I)=(I-1) *0.1875:Y(I)=SIN(X(I)):NEXT I
```

where $N=10$, you will generate a table of data for the sine function between 0 and about $\pi/2$. The interpolation will be quite precise for this range of value, but if you exceed the range of your data table, the interpolation will be so far off it will be useless. In an applications program you should make sure that the program checks the value entered for interpolation to ensure that it falls within the data table used to generate the spline function.

We have mentioned many methods for approximating functions in this chapter. Taylor series approximations are usually not optimal truncated series, but they may be close. The Taylor series for sin x and cos x converges very quickly, but extremely slowly for arctan x. Apply convergence tests too when in doubt. If you want to use a polynomial expansion to approximate a function, using linear least squares to find optimal coefficients is a reasonable approach for many functions. Newton's interpolating polynomial is a way of exactly representing a table of data, but it is not useful for large tables because polynomials are oscillatory and high-degree polynomials are slow to evaluate and subject to roundoff error. Spline functions are an excellent way to interpolate a large table of data in a smooth way, but they may not be as good as the Newton interpolating polynomial in some circumstances.

CHAPTER 6

DIFFERENTIATION AND INTEGRATION

In this chapter we shall briefly cover some useful numerical methods of differentiation and integration.

NUMERICAL DIFFERENTIATION

We have repeatedly stressed that one should use numerical derivatives only at the point of a gun, but there are times when it is necessary. The first derivative is simple and is given by the *central difference quotient* formula shown in Equation 6-1.

$$f'(x) \approx \frac{f(x+h) - f(x-h)}{2h} \tag{6-1}$$

which was discussed as Equation 2-2, in Chapter 2. There is, of course, the problem of finding a suitable step size, h. The term h should be small enough so that the slope of the line between $f(x+h)$ and $f(x-h)$ approximates the derivative of f at x. It should also be large enough so that $f(x+h)-f(x-h)$ is not so small that severe round-off error occurs. This problem can be mitigated somewhat by using higher-precision arithmetic for the values of the function, but this is not always possible. Even if it were, it does not eliminate the problem, it just moves the point at which roundoff error becomes severe.

Sometimes higher-order derivatives are also needed. Since $f''(x) = (f'(x))'$, we can apply our differentiation formulas to the $f'(x)$ as well as to $f(x)$ itself. The result is:

$$f''(x) \approx \frac{f'(x+k) - f'(x-k)}{2k} \tag{6-2}$$

$$f''(x) \approx \left(\frac{f(x+k+h) - f(x+k-h)}{2h} - \frac{f(x-k+h) - f(x-k-h)}{2h} \right)/2k \qquad (6\text{-}3)$$

Since h and k are arbitrary small steps, we can set $h=k$:

$$f''(x) \approx \frac{f(x+2h) - 2f(x) + f(x-2h)}{4h^2} \qquad (6\text{-}4)$$

for the second derivative of $f(x)$.

The derivative computational definition used in Equation 6-1 can be used recursively to define higher-order derivatives. It is possible to devise derivative formulas with different orders for the error functions and apply these definitions recursively to obtain higher-order derivative formulas. Chart 6-1 presents such a table of derivatives based on the central difference quotient formula, with an error term of the order h^2 (written $O(h^2)$).

Chart 6-1. Formulas for Derivatives

$f'(x) \approx [-f(x-h) + f(x+h)]/2h$

$f''(x) \approx [f(x-h) - 2f(x) + f(x+2h)]/4h^2$

$f'''(x) \approx [-f(x-2h) + 2f(x-h) - 3f(x+h) + fx) + f(x+3h)]/8h^3$

$f''''(x) \approx [-2f(x-2h) - 2f(x-h) + 5f(x) + f(x+h) - 4f(x+2h) + f(x-3h)$
$\qquad\qquad + f(x+4h)]/16h^4$

Program 6-1 shows the central difference quotient formulas for the first through the fourth derivatives of a function defined in line 30. It should prove interesting to examine the effect of changing the size of the step at a given point of evaluation.

Using the function exp (x) at $x=1$ Table 6-1 was produced for $h=0.1$ and $h=0.001$. Remember, the derivative of exp (x) is exp (x), which is not true for any other function, of course. Therefore the value of all the derivatives of the function should equal the value of the function at that point.

Table 6-1. Higher Numerical Derivatives

Order of Derivative	Value if $h=0.1$	Value if $h=0.001$
1	2.722 82	2.718 33
2	2.720 52	2.622 6
3	2.725 01	−119.209
4	2.737 04	238 419.0

Notice that using the smaller step size produced a more accurate value (true value is 2.718 281 828) for the first derivative but severely erroneous values for the third and fourth derivatives. The larger step size was more stable for higher-order derivatives, as you would expect from roundoff error.

Program 6-1. Numerical Derivatives

```
10 REM        EXAMPLE OF CENTRAL DIFFERENCE DERIVATIVE FOR-
              MULAS
20 REM DEFINE YOUR FUNCTION IN LINE 30
30 DEF FN F(X)=SIN(X)
40 REM GET POINT OF EVALUATION
50 INPUT"ENTER THE POINT OF EVAUATION FOR DERIVATIVES";X
60 REM GET STEP SIZE
70 INPUT"ENTER STEP SIZE FOR DIFFERENTIATION";H
80 REM CALCULATE DERIVATIVES
90 F0=FN F(X-2*H)
100 F1=FN F(X-H)
110 F=FN F(X)
120 F2=FN F(X+H)
130 F3=FN F(X+2*H)
140 REM FIRST DERIVATIVE
150 D1=(F2-F1)/2/H
160 D2=(F2-2*F+F1)/H[2
170 D3=(F3-2*F2+2*F1 -F0)/2/H[3
180 D4=(F3-4*F2 +6*F+4*F1+ F0)/H[4
190 PRINT TAB(16);"AT X=";X;" AND H=";H
200 PRINT TAB(20);"D1=";D1
210 PRINT TAB(20);"D2=";D2
220 PRINT TAB(20);"D3=";D3
230 PRINT TAB(20);"D4=";D4
240 END
```

NUMERICAL INTEGRATION

Early in this book, we developed a method for finding the area under a curve using a series of trapezoids to approximate small areas, and summing them to approximate the total area. In keeping with the overall thrust of this book, no proofs of the integration formulas will be given. For more rigorous treatment, see the references.

Simpson's Rules for Integration

If you have equally spaced table data describing the function to be integrated, there are several Simpson's rules to integrate this kind of function. Simpson's rule is presented in Equation 6-5, and the three-eighths rule is presented in Equation 6-6.

Simpson's 1/3 Rule for Integration

$$\int_{x}^{x+2h} f(x)dx \approx \frac{h}{3} \left(f(x) + 4f(x+h) + f(x+2h) \right) \qquad (6\text{-}5)$$

The 3/8 Rule for Integration

$$\int_{x}^{x+3h} f(x)dx \approx \frac{2h}{8} \left(f(x) + 3f(x+h) + 3f(x+2h) + f(x+3h) \right) \qquad (6\text{-}6)$$

Both the Simpson's and three-eighths methods have errors $O(h^5)$. They require that you have equally spaced data or that you can determine values of the function anywhere you desire. If it is the latter case, that you can evaluate the function anywhere you like, there is a more general method, called the Romberg method, that actually can be used to generate the trapezoid and Simpson methods as special cases.

The Romberg Algorithm

The Romberg method uses two separate approximations of the integral to obtain a third, more accurate one. In general, you use an approximation of step size h with another of step size $h/2$ to obtain a third with step size $h/2$. If $I_j(h)$ is an estimate of the integral with step size h, it is produced by two other estimates $I_{j-1}(h)$ and $I_{j-1}(2h)$ in the following way:

$$I_j(h) = \frac{4^j I_{j-1}(h) - I_{j-1}(2h)}{4^j - 1} \qquad (6\text{-}7)$$

which is called *Romberg iteration*.

In coding this, a "triangle" of values is produced, until either a termination test is satisfied or some maximum number of iterations is reached. Each iteration produces an estimate with half the previous step size. Normally, the user will enter an initial number of steps to use, and h is defined to be $(b-a)/n$, where n is the number of steps, and b and a are the limits of integration. An initial estimate is made using the trapezoid method and the iteration is started. When the change in the next step is smaller than some fraction of the value of the computed integral, then the termination test is satisfied.

A routine to perform Romberg integration is shown in Program 6-2.

Program 6-2. Romberg Method

```
10 REM    ROMBERG METHOD OF INTEGRATION
20 DEFINT J,K,N
```

```
30 REM DEFINE YUR FUNCTION IN LINE 30
40 DEF FN F(X)=SIN(X)
50 INPUT"LOWER AND UPPER LIMITS OF INTEGRATION";A,B
60 NR=10:INPUT"MAXIMUM NUMBER OF ROWS COMPUTED";NR
70 ND=5:INPUT"NUMBER OF SIGNIFICANT DIGITS";ND
80 REM DEFINE INITIAL STEP SIZE AND TERMINATION VALUE
90 H=(B-A)
100 RT=10↑(-ND)
110 DIM I(NR,NR)
120 REM DETERMINE FIRST TRAPEZOID ESTIMATE
130 I(1,1)=H*(FN F(A)+FN F(B))/2
140 PRINT"INITIAL ESTIMATE IS ";I(1,1)
150 L=1
160 REM NOW ITERATE
170 FOR K=2 TO NR
180 H=H/2:SUM=0:L=L+L
190 FOR J=1 TO L-1 STEP 2
200     SUM = SUM + FN F(A+H*J)
210 NEXT J
220 I(K,1) = I(K-1,1)/2 + H*SUM
230 M=1
240 FOR J=2 TO K
250 M = M * 4
260    I(K,J) = I(K,J-1) + (I(K,J-1) - I(K-1,J-1))/(M-1)
270 NEXT J
280 PRINT K"TH ITERATION ===> "I(K,K)
290 REM TERMINATION TEST
300 IF ABS(I(K,K) - I(K,K-1))><= RT*ABS(I,(K,K)) THEN 340
310 NEXT K
320 PRINT"DID NOT CONVERGE : RESULT WAS ";I(NR,NR)
330 GOTO 350
340 PRINT"CONVERGED TO ";I(K,K)
350 END
```

Integration of Data Tables

The Romberg algorithm is fine if you have a function that can be evaluated anywhere in the desired interval. It sometimes happens that this is not the case. What do you do if you have a table of data? Well, Simpson's and the three-eighths rules can be used if they are equally spaced. If they are not equally spaced, then life is more difficult.

If the points are not equally spaced, then general algorithms are difficult to devise using only the values you have. Since we have already discussed interpolation of functions, we can use this method to provide a means of approximating the function anywhere, provided that the point of evaluation is within the table. The interpolation method we recommend is the cubic spline method. A program using a cubic spline function to interpolate a function for a Romberg integration routine is given in Program 6-3.

First, you are asked for the table data points. The value at which you are taking the function is X(K), and Y(K) is the value of the function at that value. These numbers are stored and the cubic spline function is created. Control is then passed to the integration routine. You are asked for the lower and upper limits of integration, the maximum number of rows in the Romberg triangle to be produced, and the number of digits accuracy desired.

Programming niceties, such as disk or cassette i/o for storing and retrieving the data, should be added to create a real applications program. These were omitted so that the program logic would be as uncluttered as possible. Although this program is fairly long compared to the others in this book, it is primarily composed of two routines: the spline generation and the Romberg integration routine. No DEF FN or other specialized BASIC facilities are used, so it should be easy to move to any microcomputer supporting floating-point BASIC.

Program 6-3. Integration of Data Tables

```
5 REM CUBIC SPLINE-ROMBERG INTEGRATION PROGRAM
10 REM CUBICSPLINE FUNCTION GENERATOR
20 CLEAR 200:DEFINT K,J:DIM K
30 CLS:INPUT"SPLINE ANALYSIS: NUMBER OF TABLE DATA POINTS";N
40 DIM B(N),D(N),L(N),U(N),X(N),Y(N)
50 PRINT"ENTER DATA POINTS :"
60 FOR K=1 TO N
70 PRINT"X,Y FOR TABLE ENTRY #";K
80 INPUT X(K),Y(K)
90 NEXT K
100 PRINT"DATA ENTRY COMPLETE, NOW CALCULATING SPLINE FUNC-
    TION."
110 D(1)=1:U(1)=0:L(1)=0:B(1)=0
120 FOR K=2 TO N−1
130    D(K)=2*(X(K+1)−X(K−1))
140    U(K)=X(K+1)−X(K)
150    L(K)=U(K):REM SINCE THE MATRIX IS SYMMETRIC
160    T=(Y(K+1)−Y(K))/U(K)
170    B(K)=6*(T−(Y(K)−Y(K−1))/(X(K)−X(K−1)))
180 NEXT K
190 D(N)=1:U(N−1)=0:L(N−1)=0:B(N)=0
200 REM SOLVE SYMMETRIC TRIDIAGONAL SYSTEM
210 GOSUB 400
220 REM GOTO INTEGRATION ROUTINE
230 GOTO 620
```

```
240 REM INTERPOLATATION ROUTINE FROM SPLINE FUNCTION
250 REM X IS THE VALUE TO INTERPOLATE FROM
260 REM FIRST, FIND WHICH INTERVAL IT IS (K=INTERVAL NUMBER)
270 FOR J1=1 TO N-2
280 K1=N-J1
290 IF X-X(K1)>=0 THEN T=X-X(K1):GOTO 340
300 NEXT J
310 REM IF IT GETS HERE, THEN X IS IN THE FIRST INTERVAL
320 K1=1:T=X-X(1)
330 REM INTERPOLATE FROM SPLINE IN INTERVAL # K
340 H1=X(K1+1)-X(K1)
350 A1=T*(B(K1+1)-B(K1))/6/H1 + B(K1)/2
360 B1=T*A+ (Y(K1+1)-Y(K1))/H1-H1*(2*B(K1)+B(K1+1))/6
370 SP=T*B1+Y(K1)
380 REM SP = RESULT OF INTERPOLATION
390 RETURN
400 REM TRI-DIAG ROUTINE
410 REM SOLVES A TRIDIAGONAL SYSTEM OF EQUATIONS
420 REM B( ) HOLDS THE CONSTANTS OF THE EQUATIONS
430 REM D( ) HOLDS THE MAIN DIAGONAL COEFFICIENTS
440 REM L( ) HOLDS THE LOWER DIAGONAL COEFFICIENTS
450 REM U( ) HOLDS THE UPPER DIAGONAL COEFFICIENTS
460 REM IN THIS CASE, THE MATRIX IS SYMMETRICAL,
470 REM THEREFORE, U(K)=L(K)
480 REM N=NUMBER OF EQUATIONS TO SOLVE
490 FOR K=2 TO N
500 X=L(K-1)/D(K-1)
510 D(K)=D(K)-X*U(K-1)
520 B(K)=B(K)-X*B(K-1)
530 NEXT K
540 B(N)=B(N)/D(N)
550 REM NOW BACKWARDS SUBSTITUTION
560 FOR K=1 TO N-1
570 B(N-K)=(B(N-K)-U(N-K)* B(N-K+1)))/D(N-K)
580 NEXT K
590 REM COEFFICIENTS FOR SPLINE FUNCTION ARE STORED IN B(I)
600 RETURN
610 REM
620 REM      ROMBERG METHOD OF INTEGRATION
630 REM
640 REM USES THE SPLINE FUNCTION FOR INTERPOLATION OF TABLE
650 INPUT"LOWER AND UPPER LIMITS OF INTEGRATION";A,B
660 IF (A<X(1)) OR (B>X(N)) THEN
    PRINT"OUTSIDE LIMITS OF TABLE":GOTO 650
670 NR=10:INPUT"MAXIMUM NUMBER OF ROWS COMPUTED";NR
680 ND=5:INPUT"NUMBER OF SIGNIFICANT DIGITS";ND
690 REM DEFINE INITIAL STEP SIZE AND TERMINATION VALUE
700 H=B-A
710 RT=10↑(-ND)
720 DIM I(NR,NR)
```

```
730 REM DETERMINE FIRST TRAPEZOID ESTIMATE
740 REM GET FUNCTION VALUES
750 X=A:GOSUB 270:F1=SP:X=B:GOSUB 270:F2=SP
760 I(1,1)=H*(F1+F2)/2
770 PRINT"INITIAL ESTIMATE IS ";I(1,1)
780 L=1
790 REM NOW ITERATE
800 FOR K=2 TO NR
810    H=H/2:SUM=0:L=L+L
820    FOR J=1 TO L-1 STEP 2
830       X=A+H*J:GOSUB 270
840       SUM = SUM + SP
850    NEXT J
860    I(K,1) = I(K-1,1)/2 + H*SUM
870    M=1
880    FOR J=2 TO K
890       M = M * 4
900       I(K,J) = I(K,J-1) +(I(K,J-1) - I(K-1,J-1))/(M-1)
910    NEXT J
920    PRINT K"TH ITERATION ===> ";I(K,K)
930    REM TERMINATION TEST
940    IF ABS(I(K,K) - I(K,K-1))<= RT*ABS(I(K,K)) THEN 980
950 NEXT K
960 PRINT"DID NOT CONVERGE " RESULT WAS ";I(NR,NR)
970 GOTO 990
980 PRINT"CONVERGED TO ";I(K,K)
990 END
```

Example Output From Table Integration

Table 6-2 shows the X(K) and Y(K) values constituting a table of values for the sin x function. Twenty equally spaced values were used (although they could have been unequally spaced as well). These values were used to integrate the function from 0 to $\pi/2$. This definite integral is, of course, 1.0000. Despite the fact that we only had twenty values in the table, and only ten of these are in the range of the integration, the integral is fairly accurate, particularly considering the fact that almost all the values used in the Romberg integration procedure were interpolated.

The integration of Table 6-2 from $x=0$ to $x=\pi/2$ is as follows:

The initial estimate is:	0.786 05
The second iteration:	1.006 31
The third iteration:	1.007 25
The fourth iteration:	1.004 02
The fifth iteration:	1.003 88
This converges to:	1.003 88

Table 6-2.
Table of Sine Values

x	sin x
0.000 00	0.000 00
0.170 00	0.169 18
0.340 00	0.333 49
0.510 00	0.488 18
0.680 00	0.628 79
0.850 00	0.751 28
1.020 00	0.852 11
1.190 00	0.928 37
1.360 00	0.977 86
1.530 00	0.999 17
1.700 00	0.991 66
1.870 00	0.955 57
2.040 00	0.891 93
2.210 00	0.802 57
2.380 00	0.690 07
2.550 00	0.557 68
2.720 00	0.409 21
2.890 00	0.248 95
3.060 00	0.081 50
3.230 00	−0.088 29

Table 6-3.
Extended Table of Sine Values

x	sin x
0.000 00	0.000 00
0.085 00	0.084 90
0.170 00	0.169 18
0.255 00	0.252 25
0.340 00	0.333 49
0.425 00	0.412 32
0.510 00	0.488 18
0.595 00	0.560 51
0.680 00	0.628 79
0.765 00	0.692 54
0.850 00	0.751 28
0.935 00	0.804 60
1.020 00	0.852 11
1.105 00	0.893 46
1.190 00	0.928 37
1.275 00	0.956 57
1.360 00	0.977 86
1.445 00	0.992 10
1.530 00	0.999 17
1.615 00	0.999 02

The table values in Table 6-2 range from 0 to 3.23. A table with more values in the desired range is shown in Table 6-3. Here the values range from 0 to 1.7. The integral was still taken from 0 to $\pi/2$. The integration of Table 6-3 from $x=0$ to $x=\pi/2$ is as follows:

The initial estimate is:	0.785 84
The second iteration:	1.002 58
The third iteration:	1.001 71
The fourth iteration:	1.001 08
This converges to:	1.001 08

You can see the end result in Table 6-2 is improved by 0.0028, or 0.3 percent, by using the values from Table 6-3. The difference is not that marked. Both methods can be improved by using double precision for the table values and the variables used in the BASIC program, but the second table will show a greater improvement.

We have examined numerical differentiation and integration in more depth now, but the topics are hardly depleted. More advanced methods can be found in the references.

CHAPTER 7

OUTPUTTING THE RESULTS

An important part of numerical analysis is interfacing the programs with the humans that want to understand the results. There are usually several ways to do this, such as displaying a table of values, plotting a graph of the solution, histograms, pie charts, etc. Often, one method of output is more appropriate than another and, perhaps more often, two or more modes of output may be required to show the information necessary.

Suppose you are modelling a stochastic (random) process that generates a normal distribution. A table of numbers may be necessary for some purposes, but can a table of numbers really *look* normally distributed? A histogram, or bar chart, is usually better for that. Or, suppose you are solving a differential equation (a topic discussed in the next chapter). It might be nice to output the results not only as a table of results, but also as a real-time plot, that is, a plot that displays each data point as it is being generated. Then, there is still the problem of the device. Do you want to plot your figures (scatter plots, histograms, etc.) on the video screen, on a computer printer, or both? It may often be quite useful to send different types of output to different devices. In solving a differential equation you may want to do a real-time plot on the video screen, a plot of the integral on the printer, and send the table of values to a disk file, all at the same time.

The screen graphics programs developed here are specifically designed for the TRS-80 Models I and III, but since we are concerned with the concepts involved in generating algorithms for graphics software, it will be easy to translate the graphics from one computer to another. The BASIC language is not particularly standardized, and this is especially true for graphics. The TRS-80 has only simple graphics commands: SET, RESET, and POINT. It does not have the vector graphics available on the Apple and Atari computers, for example. By designing the software to run on the TRS-80, we will use features that are available on many other computers, even though their syntax may be different. Thus it should be easy to move the programs developed here to other computers. The printer software will work on other computers and printers, since it uses no special features. The printer functions used are LPRINT to send data to the line printer and various string functions to set characters within strings. These are briefly described in Appendix A.

To produce maximum quality of plots on the printers, you should make sure that your printer is in a nonproportional (monospace) font and prints unidirectionally. For printers that support proportional and bidirectional printing, there are normally DIP switches that can be set to toggle and/or software "escape sequences" so that they may be changed by sending a sequence of bytes to the printer. Check with your printer manual.

TRS-80 SCREEN GRAPHICS

The TRS-80 has several graphics commands available. These are:

1. CLS—clears the screen.
2. SET(x,y)—sets (turns on) the point with the coordinates (x,y).
3. RESET(x,y)—resets (turns off) the point with the coordinates (x,y).
4. POINT(x,y)—returns a TRUE (−1) if the point is SET, otherwise returns a FALSE (0).

The TRS-80 video screen has horizontal coordinates from 0 to 127, and vertical coordinates from 0 to 47, for a total of 6144 points that may be SET or RESET. The upper-left corner is (0,0). The y coordinate increases as you move down the screen, and the x coordinate increases as you move across the screen to the right. This is a mirror image of the normal Cartesian coordinate system in which up represents an increase in the y coordinate. We will reverse this mirror image by changing the direction of our plots.

Translation means that we move the coordinate system around. The "middle" of the screen is the point (64,24). If we want to plot a graph in which the middle of the screen is (0,0) (a normal Cartesian graph), then we will have to add 64 to each x coordinate and 24 to each y

coordinate that we plot. This will effectively move the point (0,0) from the upper-left corner of the screen to the middle. If we apply this addition to each point in the graph, we have moved, or translated, it in space.

Usually, we will also want to *scale* our plots to the screen. Since we have 128 points horizontally and 48 points vertically, plots "bigger" than this will fall off the screen, and plots smaller than this may be so small that they fail to convey information. By appropriately scaling the plot (making it bigger or smaller), we can reach some optimal size for our plots.

Depending on how we decide to scale the plot, we may still have points on our plot fall off the screen. If we attempt to manipulate these points that really are not on the screen, we will get an illegal function error. We must sometimes *clip* the values of our plots so that the program can recognize points that fall off the screen and not attempt to plot them.

We will use the ideas of translation, scaling, and clipping in all our programs, whether they plot on the screen or on a printer.

Unlike on some other computers, to draw a line on the TRS-80 screen requires a loop. Normally, a FOR-NEXT loop is used. The routine is Program 7-1, which is a short routine that draws a line between two points. It is a simple routine, and assumes that all points in the line are contained in the screen. This need not be the case. Even if both end points of the line are off the screen, some part of the line may be on the screen. However, that is a bit more advanced.

Program 7-1. Line Drawing

```
1000 REM Draw line from (x1,y1) to (x2,y2)
1010 REM check endpoints for legality
1020 IF (X1<0) OR (X1>127) THEN GOTO 1130
1030 IF (X2<0) OR (X2>127) THEN GOTO 1130
1040 IF (Y1<0) OR (Y1>47) THEN GOTO 1130
1050 IF (Y2<0) OR (Y2>47) THEN GOTO 1130
1060 REM compute slope
1070 IF X1<>X2 THEN SL=(Y2−Y1)/(X2−X1):SG=SGN(SL) ELSE 1150:REM
        if not, it must be vertical line
1080 REM compute intercept
1090 B=Y1−SL*X1
1100 FOR I=X1 TO X2 STEP SG
1110     SET(I,SL*I+B)
1120 NEXT I
1130 RETURN
1140 REM vertical line
1150 FOR I=Y1 TO Y2 STEP SGN(Y2−Y1)
```

```
1160 SET(X1,I)
1170 NEXT I
1180 GOTO 1130
```

Some BASICs, such as Atari BASIC, have the DRAWTO command, and so most of Program 7-1 can be written as in Program 7-2.

Program 7-2. Line Drawing With DRAWTO Command

```
1000 REM Draw line from (x1,y1) to (x2,y2)
1010 REM in Atari Basic, graphics mode 8, color 1
1020 IF (X1<0) OR (X1>319) THEN GOTO 1080
1030 IF (X2<0) OR (X2>319) THEN GOTO 1080
1040 IF (Y1<0) OR (Y1>191) THEN GOTO 1080
1050 IF (Y2<0) OR (Y2>191) THEN GOTO 1080
1060 PLOT X1,Y1
1070 DRAWTO X2,Y2
1080 RETURN
```

So you can see that the routine can be easily moved to other computers.

There are many topics in graphics that will not be mentioned here, such as perspective, removal of hidden lines, and animation. They are more appropriately discussed in a book devoted to graphics. In this chapter we will discuss a number of elementary graphical techniques, including:

1. scatter plots
2. histograms and bar charts
3. pie charts

We will cover each topic separately and develop routines for both screen and printer graphics for each. We will then discuss a few considerations about generating tables and reports on line printers. As far as we are concerned, the only function of graphics is to change data from a system into knowledge about the system.

Any printer on the market will be able to print the plots we will design here. We will generally use no more complex printer function than LPRINT to send output to the printer. You may find it useful to change font from 10 or 12 characters per inch (cpi) to 16 cpi, since you can put more on a page, provided that your printer supports the feature. Many printers have bit-graphics capabilities and a variety of fonts and special characters. Because these are not at all standardized, we will avoid them here. The graphical concepts used to generate the following routines can generally be easily adapted to support bit-graphics and the other special features of any given printer.

SCATTER PLOTS

Scatter plots are plots in which data sets or functions are plotted on the device according to a coordinate system. The most popular coordinate system is the linear distance ("rectilinear") coordinate system called Cartesian after the mathematician (and would-be philosopher) Rene Descartes. Plots using the normal Cartesian coordinate system are also called x,y plots. Typical scatter plots are shown in Fig. 7–1. Scatter plots provide a simple means of presenting data in an intelligible form.

We will begin with simple rectilinear plots, the kind you normally think of as a data plot (see Fig. 7-1). First, let's draw the coordinate system. But where? We will follow mathematical convention and place the origin of the coordinate system either in the middle, with the x and y axes forming a cross $(+)$, or in the lower left-hand corner so that going to the right means an increase in x and going up means an increase in y. As mentioned earlier, the direction of the y axis is opposite of the normal TRS-80 screen, which was designed with the y axis increasing as you go down the screen. This is easy to handle. Basically, rather than plot (x,y), we will plot the point $(x,n-y)$, where n is the TRS-80 screen coordinate of the y axis. If the origin is in the middle of the screen, then we will plot $(64+x,24-y)$, since the "soft" origin of the coordinate system appears at the physical screen coordinates $(64,24)$. For example, to plot the point $(1,1)$ with the origin in the center of the screen, we would actually set the TRS-80 screen coordinate $(64+1,24-1)$, or $(65,23)$. If the origin is at the lower left corner, we will plot $(x,47-y)$, since the origin occurs at the physical screen coordinates $(0,47)$. By subtracting in $n-y$ we change the direction "up" from a physical direction down the screen to up the screen. It is easier for humans to interpret plots thus rescaled.

Program 7-3 draws the coordinate system of the screen. The first routine puts the origin at $(64,24)$ and assigns the translation coordinate variables $(xt,yt)=(64,24)$, so that the data are plotted about an origin in the middle of the screen. The second routine places the origin at the lower left-hand corner of the screen, and adjusts the value of (xt,yt) accordingly.

Program 7-3. Coordinate System Drawing

```
830 REM Sample 'driver' program using the routines to
840 REM plot points
850 REM generate points
860 N=100:PI=3.14159265*2:DIM X(N),Y(N)
```

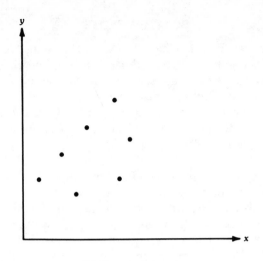

(A) Discrete data points.

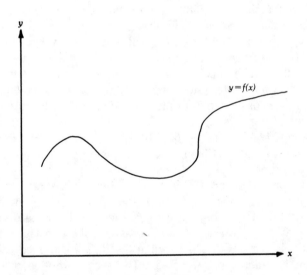

(B) An arbitrary function.

Fig. 7-1. Plots in rectangular coordinates.

```
870 FOR I=1 TO N:X(I)=RND(0)*PI:Y(I) =SIN(X(I)):NEXT I
880 REM Choose coordinate system
890 PRINT"1. origin in middle  2. origin in lower corner"
900 INPUT J:IF J=2 THEN 950 ELSE IF J<>1 THEN 890
910 CLS:GOSUB 1000:GOSUB 1220:GOSUB 1350
```

```
920 FOR I=1 TO N:X=X(I):Y=Y(I):GOSUB 1420''NEXT I
930 PRINT@0,"*";
940 GOTO 940
950 REM
960 CLS:GOSUB 1110:GOSUB 1220:GOSUB 1300
970 FOR I=1 TO N:X=X(I):Y=Y(I):GOSUB 1420:NEXT I
980 PRINT@0,"*";
990 GOTO 990
1000 REM Draw coordinate system in the middle
1010 REM Translation variables
1020 XT=64:YT=24
1030 FOR I=0 TO 127
1040    SET(I,YT)
1050 NEXT I
1060 FOR I=0 TO 47
1070    SET(XT,I)
1080 NEXT I:RETURN
1090 REM Draw coordinate system at lower left corner
1100 REM translation variables
1110 XT=0:YT=47
1120 REM Draw x axis
1130 FOR I=0 TO 127
1140    SET(I,YT)
1150 NEXT I
1160 REM Draw y axis
1170 FOR I=0 TO 47
1180    SET(XT,I)
1190 NEXT I
1200 REM find largest and smallest values
1210 REM N=the number of points in the arrays X(i),Y(i)
1220 UX=X(1):LX=UX:UY=Y(1):LY=UY
1230 DEF FN MA(A,B)=-(ABS(A)>ABS(B))*A -(ABS(B)=>ABS(A))*B
1240 FOR I=2 TO N
1250    IF X(I)>UX THEN UX=X(I)
1260    IF Y(I)>UY THEN UY=Y(I)
1270    IF X(I)<LX THEN LX=X(I)
1280    IF Y(I)<LY THEN LY=Y(I)
1290 NEXT I:RETURN
1300 REM Now, find the scaling factors for corner origin
1310 IF UX=LX OR UY=LY THEN1460:REM exit if error
1320 XS=127/(UX-LX):XI=-127*LX/(UX-LX)
1330 YS=47/(UY-LY):YI=-47*LY/(UY-LY)
1340 RETURN
1350 REM scale for the axis in the middle
1360 IF UX=LX OR UY=LY THEN1460:REM EXIT IF ERROR
1370 GX=FN MAX(UX,LX):GY=FN MAX(UY,LY)
1380 XS=63/GX:XI=0
1390 YS=24/GY:YI=0
1400 RETURN
1410 REM Routine to set points on the screen
```

```
1420 REM Call each time you wish to set a point (x,y)
1430 XP=X*XS+XI+XT:YP= YT-(Y*YS+YI)
1440 IF (XP<0) OR (XP>127) OR (YP<0) OR (YP>47) THEN 1460
1450 SET (XP,YP)
1460 RETURN
```

The next task is to scale the graph. We will assume here that you want all the points of a data table in the graph. You must then determine the largest and the smallest data points. If your data is presorted, this is easy. If not, then just run the routine in lines 1200–1290 to find the largest and smallest points and the scaling factors for the x and y coordinates.

These routines may be called by a BASIC program that generates N data points, with the N x values in the X(I) array, and the corresponding y values in Y(I). The routines in the program scale the screen so that all the points may be represented. The last routine actually sets them. This latter routine is general purpose, since it will translate and scale the coordinates of the screen using the previously determined translation and scaling factors. The point is then tested for legality. If it is legal, then it is set. This prevents an inadvertent ILLEGAL FUNCTION error by attempting to set a point that sits off the physical screen. The initial portion of the program is a "driver" program that generates the points to plot and then calls the BASIC subroutines to set up the screen and plot the points. A sample data set is calculated and then plotted.

How does one send this kind of a plot to a line printer? Typically, only one axis is scaled (across the paper width) and the plot scrolls as far as it needs to go. This approach is most appropriate for large plots, or plots in which you don't know the range of one of the axes ahead of time. For example, if you are doing a real-time plot of points being generated, say, by a simulation, it is easiest to print out the plot by scrolling each line forward. Many, if not most, computer programs use this method.

For plots in which you know before plotting the data the number and range of your data points, however, it is often much more visually pleasing to set up your plot just as you set up the screen plot, scaling and translating both axes for optimal effect. This is more difficult with a general printer, because many printers do not have reverse line feeds. This requires that you sort your data and determine all the points that need to be plotted on a print line before sending that line to the printer. This will include the axis line (if desired) and any data points. If you plot sin x, and scale the y axis for values between −1 and 1, then most of the print lines will contain more than one data point. This means that you must scan ahead through your data to determine which points fall on a specific print line and only then send it to the printer. You can see that this is not useful for real-time plots. You must be able to scan through your data to use this method.

The data need not be wholly contained in your computer's main memory. It can be stored on a disk file and searched through without loading all the data points into memory. For simplicity we will assume there is enough memory to hold all the data points. An extensive discussion of managing data belongs in a textbook on data base management and is not appropriate here. Therefore we will use only the bubble sort (because of its conceptual simplicity). There are many faster sorts available, and you should feel free to substitute a faster method in your application programs.

We will plot our data on the printer so that the x axis goes across the width of the page and the y axis goes along the length of the page. In our simple Program 7-4 you will be asked for the width of your printer. This, of course, varies with your printer and the font used to print. The standard is 80 characters per line total and the standard page length is 60 lines of text on a 66 physical line page (we have to allow for margins, after all). The program will allow you to insert the axes or not, as your heart desires. Program 7-4 is not meant to be a plot program for all purposes, but should show a simple way to generate visually attractive and informative plots of functions and data on your printer.

Program 7-4 will autoscale your plot, if desired. This means that it will scan through the data and determine the lower and upper x and y limits and scale the plot so that all these points will fit on the plot. (Some points may be discarded because of rounding if they fall on a boundary. A message is printed each time a data point is discarded.) If you choose to enter the limits yourself, you can set the limits so that all or only part of your data will be plotted. You will be asked for the width of the plot and the number of print lines in the plot. Thus you can have plots that take a full page, or merely a corner. A title is centered and printed at the top of the plot.

The plot program uses string functions extensively, as do all the printer routines in this chapter. It creates an array of strings, P$(I). Each string is one line that will be sent to the printer. If you lack enough memory to do this, it should be easy to rewrite the program so that it stores the strings to disk or cassette rather than keeping them all in memory before printing them.

You also have the option of labelling the y axis with the values. You must enter the number of digits to the left and to the right of the decimal point. The program uses the BASIC function PRINT USING "####.###" to format the numbers. The given string "####.###" will always print four digits to the left of the decimal point and three to the right. If there are not enough digits to the left, then blanks are printed; if there are not enough digits to the right, then zeros are printed. If your BASIC lacks the PRINT USING function, there are a couple of things you can do.

Since the format statement is included in the left and right margin strings, LM$ and RM$, you can delete the right and left margins totally from your plot. Everytime you see an LPRINT USING, change it to an LPRINT. Everytime you see an LM$ or RM$ being printed, just replace it with a single blank," ".

Alternatively, you can change the y label number to a string and process it in a subroutine. Most BASICs do permit this type of conversion. Then, just pad it on the left and right so that the total length of the string is the same as some constant value. Now, when it is printed, followed by the plot line, the plot lines will all line up. A sample plot is shown in Fig. 7-2.

Program 7-4. Printer XY Plot

```
10 CLEAR5000:N=30:PI=3.14159265:DIM X(N),Y(N)
20 REM SAMPLE DATA POINTS:
30 FOR I=1 TO N:X(I)=RND(0)*PI*(−1)↑RND(2):
   Y(I)=SIN(X(I)):NEXT I
40 REM PRINT IT
50 GOSUB 90:REM GET PLOT PARAMETERS
60 GOSUB 480:REM CALCULATE AND PLOT
70 INPUT"READY FOR HARDCOPY (Y/N)";A$:
   IF A$="Y" THEN GOSUB 730
80 END
90 REM GET PLOT PARAMETERS
100 REM FN CN$(A$,W) CENTERS STRING A$ IN A FIELD OF WIDTH W
110 DEF FN CN$(A$,W)=STRING$((W−LEN (A$))/2,32)+A$
120 INPUT"PLOTTING CHARACTER";PC$
130 INPUT"TITLE OF PLOT";TI$
140 INPUT"INCLUDE AXES IN PLOT (Y/N)";AQ$
150 INPUT"INCLUDE VALUES ON Y AXIS (Y/N)";AZ$
160 IF AZ$="Y" THEN INPUT"Y AXIS LABEL: NUMBER OF DIGITS TO
    LEFT AND RIGHT OF DECIMAL
    POINT";YM,YN:UY$=STRING$(YM,"#"):
    IF YN>0 THEN UY$=UY$+"."+STRING$(YN,"#")
170 INPUT"ENTER LEFT MARGIN";LM:IF LM=0 AND AZ$<>"Y" THEN 200
180 IF LM<LEN(UY$) THEN "TOO SHORT TO CONTAIN Y LABEL":GOTO 170
190 LM$=UY$+STRING$(LM−LEN(UY$),32)+" :"
```

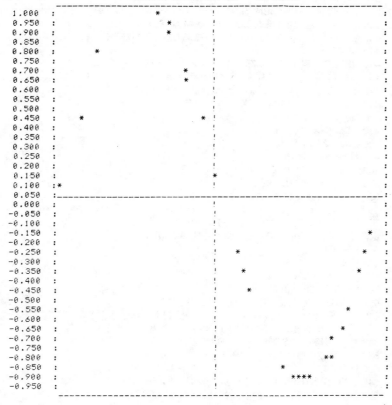

Fig. 7-2. A printer plot.

```
200 RM$=":"
210 INPUT"TOTAL PLOT WIDTH (INCLUDING LEFT MARGIN)";WT
220 WP=WT-RM-LM+1:REM WP =WIDTH OF PLOT ITSELF
230 INPUT"NUMBER OF PRINT LINES IN PLOT";PL
240 INPUT"1. ENTER PLOT RANGES    OR   2. AUTOSCALE PLOT";C
250 IF C=2 THEN 330 ELSE IF C<>1 THEN 240
260 INPUT"ENTER LOWER X LIMIT";XL
270 INPUT"ENTER UPPER X LIMIT";XU
280 INPUT"ENTER LOWER Y LIMIT";YL
290 INPUT"ENTER UPPER Y LIMIT";YU
300 GOTO 430:REM PLOT IT
310 REM AUTOSCALE PLOT
320 REM GET UPPER/LOWER LIMITS FOR Y
330 YL=Y(1):YU=Y(1)
340 REM AND X
350 XL=X(1):XU=X(1)
360 FOR I=1 TO N
```

127

```
370    IF XL>X(I) THEN XL=X(I):REM LOWER LIMIT OF X
380    IF YL>Y(I) THEN YL=Y(I):REM LOWER LIMIT OF Y
390    IF XU<X(I) THEN XU=X(I):REM UPPER LIMIT OF X
400    IF YU<Y(I) THEN YU=Y(I):REM UPPER LIMIT OF Y
410 NEXT I
420 REM CALCULATE THE PLOT SCALING FACTORS
430 XS=WP/(XU-XL):XI=-WP *XL/(XU-XL)
440 YS=PL/(YU-YL):YI=-PL* YL/(YU-YL)
450 YC=(YU-YL)/PL:XC=(XU- XL)/WP
460 RETURN
470 REM CALCULATE PLOT
480 DIM P$(PL)
490 FOR I=0 TO PL
500    P$(I)=STRING$(WP,32)
510    REM PLOT AXES IF AQ$="Y"
520    IF AQ$<>"Y" THEN 550
530    YD=YU-YC*(I-1):IF ((YD+YC)=>0 AND (YD<=0)) AND I>0
       THEN P$(I-1)=STRING$(WP,95)
540    IF (XL<0) AND (XU>0) THEN MID$(P$(I),XI,1)="!"
550 NEXT I
560 FOR I=1 TO N
570    YP=PL-(YS*Y(I)+YI)
580    XP=XS*X(I)+XI+1
590    REM IS THE POINT ON THE PLOT?
600    IF (XP<1) OR (XP>WP) OR (YP<0) OR (YP>PL)
           THEN PRINT"DATA POINT "I" OMITTED":GOTO 630
610    REM OK, SO WHICH PRINT LINE IS IT ON?
620    MID$(P$(YP),XP,1)=PC$
630 NEXT I
640 LPRINT STRING$(LEN(LM$),32);FN CN$(TI$,WP)
650 LPRINT STRING$(LEN(LM$),32);STRING$(WP,95)
660 FOR I=0 TO PL
670   IF AZ$="Y" THEN LPRINT USING LM$;YU-I*YC;
          ELSE LPRINT LM$;
680   LPRINT P$(I);RM$
690 NEXT I
700 LPRINT STRING$(LEN(LM$),32); STRING$(WP,"-")
710 RETURN
720 REM HARDCOPY OF DATA
730 LPRINT STRING$(LEN(LM$),32);FN CN$(TI$,WP)
740 LPRINT " I";"  X","  Y":
    U$="###":UX$="###### .######"
750 FOR I=1 TO N:LPRINT USING U$;I,:
    LPRINT USING UX$;X(I),:LPRINT USING UX$;Y(I):NEXT I
760 RETURN
```

We now have two admittedly simple programs for plotting data: one to plot on the screen and one for the printer. Sometimes, log-linear or log-log plots are more convenient. This is true when the range for one (or both, in the case of log-log plots) of the variables is large or logarithmic in nature. In the latter case the curve in rectilinear coordinates will become a straight line in logarithmic coordinates. Setting up such a plot is quite simple. All you need to do to plot this is apply a transformation to one (or both) of the variables, such as

```
FOR I=1 TO N:Y(I)=LOG(Y(I)):NEXT 1
```

Just be sure that Y(I) is never zero; you can add a constant to avoid this problem, just to be sure. Then, just proceed with your plot. Remember that the final plot will be log-linear or log-log. That means that for every unit increase, the value of the original variable increases by an e-fold (e is the transcendental-number basis for Naperian logarithms). If you want a tenfold increase for each unit increase in the transformed variable, then divide the transformed variable by LN(10)=2.302585.

POLAR COORDINATES

An alternative to Cartesian coordinates are the polar coordinates. Polar coordinates reference points in a plane differently from Cartesian coordinates. Cartesian coordinates use two length values, x and y, which refer to positions along axes. Polar coordinates reference a point by an angle and a distance from zero. In Fig. 7-3 we see that an arbitrary point in the plane is referenced with a distance, r, and an angle, t.

You probably remember from elementary trigonometry the relationship between the two coordinate systems:

$$x = r \cos t$$

$$y = r \sin t$$

where
　　x and y are the axes of the Cartesian coordinate system,
　　r is called the modulus of the point,
　　t is called the amplitude of the point.

If it is so simple to convert to rectilinear coordinates, why use polar coordinates? Many functions can be written more concisely in polar form. Consider the equation for a circle. In polar form it is merely

$$r = c$$

where c is a constant. This is simpler than the rectilinear formulation $(x^2+y^2=c^2)$. A spiral can also be represented easily. A spiral is a function in which the distance (r) from the origin is a function of the angle, or amplitude, (t). For example,

$$r = at$$

where a is a constant, will plot a spiral. By changing the value of a you can make the spiral tighter or looser. You can create a rose with the simple equation

$$r = t \sin t \cos t$$

It is recommended that when you plot polar equations, you step through the angle and convert the r and t values to x and y values. Then you can easily use the programs developed previously. For example, see Program 7-5.

Program 7-5. Spirals

```
10 REM place your polar equation in line 20
20 DEF FN EQ(R,T)=R*T/3:REM spiral for example
30 DEF FN X(R,T)=R * COS(T)
40 DEF FN Y(R,T)=R * SIN(T)
50 DIM X(100),Y(100)
60 T=0
70 FOR I=1 TO 100
80     R=FN EQ(R,T)
```

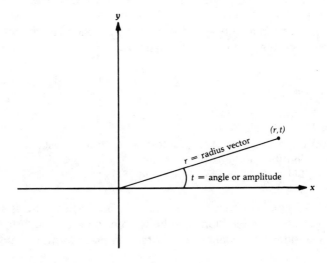

Fig. 7-3. Polar coordinates.

```
90      X(I)=FN X(R,T)
100     Y(I)=FN Y(R,T)
110     T=T+0.02
120 NEXT I
```

The data generated by Program 7-5 can be plotted with either of the previous programs.

HISTOGRAMS AND BAR CHARTS

If your data is categorical in nature, rather than continuous, then a scatter plot is not really appropriate. A bar chart is a plot of category versus number of entries in the category. A histogram is another name for a bar chart. A sample histogram is shown in Fig. 7-4.

The first step is to categorize your data. If your data is from a categorical variable, such as sex or race, then it is easy to write a routine to add "1" to a "bin" for a category each time a certain value, such as "Indian" occurs. If you have continuous variables, such as weight, from which to make categories, such as light, middleweight, and heavy, then you can set up a loop and use Boolean operators to make comparisons, such as in Program 7-6.

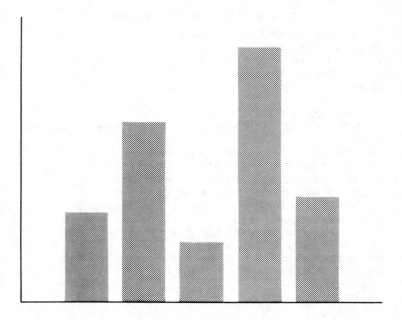

Fig. 7-4. Histogram.

Program 7-6. Categorizing Data

```
10 REM categorize your variables
20 FOR I=1 TO N
30    IF A(I)<20 THEN C(0)=C(0)+1:REM Youngsters
40    IF A(I)=>20 AND A(I)<60 THEN C(1)=C(1)+1:
      REM Middle-aged folks
50    IF A(I)=>60 THEN C(2)=C(2)+1:REM Oldsters
60 NEXT I
```

That part is easy. The plotting part is also easy, but is a little more involved. How wide should each category bar be on the histogram? How high should it go? Do you want to go up the screen or down the screen with increasing values? As with other forms of data management, there are many questions to be decided before you can continue. We will scale our video histograms so that they take up the entire screen in both directions. We will leave one line at the bottom of the screen for labelling the categories. The bars will go up the screen with increasing values. In Program 7-7 we will assume that there are a total of N categories, and the data are already placed in the array C(I), so that the value of C(I) is the number of entries in that category.

Program 7-7. Histogram Program

```
10 REM SAMPLE DATA FOR HISTOGRAMS
20 N=RND(10):DIM C(N)
30 FOR I=1 TO N
40    C(I)=RND(30)
50 NEXT I:WP=127:IN=3
60 GOSUB 1000:REM PLOT IT
65 GOSUB 1230:REM LABEL PLOTS
70 A$=INKEY$:IF A$=" " THEN 70 ELSE IF A$<>"N" THEN CLEAR:GOTO10
80 END
1000 REM SCREEN HISTOGRAM PLOT ROUTINE
1010 REM N=NUMBER OF CATEGORIES, WP=PLOT
      WIDTH,IN=WIDTH OF INTERVAL BETWEEN BARS
1020 BW=INT((WP-N*IN)/N):REM BAR WIDTH
1030 MH=C(1):LH=C(1):REM FIND MAX AND MINIMUM HEIGHT
1040 FOR I=1 TO N
1050    IF C(I)<MH THEN MH=C(I)
1060    IF C(I)<LH THEN LH=C(I)
1070 NEXT I
1080 REM SC=SCALE FACTOR
1090 SC=43/MH
1100 REM NOW PLOT IT
1110 CLS:PO=IN
1120 FOR I=1 TO N
```

```
1125    P=INT(SC*C(I))
1130   FOR J=1 TO BW
1150     FOR K=43-P TO 43
1160       SET(PO,K)
1170     NEXT K
1180     PO=PO+1
1190   NEXT J
1200   PO=PO+IN
1210 NEXT I
1220 RETURN
1230 REM LABEL N PLOTS
1235 REM CENTER LABEL UNDER BARS
1240 BP=INT(BW/2):IM=(IN/2+.4): PO=960+IM:
     L=LEN(STR$(MH)):BQ=INT((BP- L-1)/2):IF BQ>0 THEN PO=PO+BQ
1250 FOR I=1 TO N
1260   PRINT@PO,C(I);
1270   PO=PO+IM+BP
1280 NEXT I
1290 RETURN
```

This is easy to perform on the printer as well. In order to expose you to different methods, Program 7-8 makes a histogram on the printer, but does it horizontally rather than vertically. Again, rather than show every possible permutation for generating these graphics plots, it is more appropriate to show a variety of simple programs illustrating techniques, so that you can then create your own applications programs.

As with all the printer programs presented here, extensive use of string functions is made. This is done for two reasons. First, the programs are shorter than writing separate routines for each string function. Second, and more important, the "higher" the level of the functions, the easier it is to see what the function is doing. BASIC does not support procedures and supports only a rudimentary type of function declaration. By programming in terms of functions, both intrinsic in the BASIC and user-defined, we make the program "higher-order," because we are defining our program in terms closer to our own way of thinking about the problem. For example, suppose your BASIC does not have the PRINT USING function for formatting output. The TRS-80 and most other computers using Microsoft BASIC do have this, but there are others such as the Apple, that do not. If you are a TRS-80 disk owner, you can use the programs as is, but if you are an Apple owner, you must either write routines to perform the PRINT USING function, or just use a PRINT statement, and not worry about the pretty output format. Nevertheless, by using the advanced functions we use conceptually simple building blocks for our programs, making them easier to read than if we wrote subroutines for each and every advanced BASIC function, using the weakest possible BASIC as a common starting ground.

Program 7-8 uses 2000 bytes of string space. This may be increased or decreased as needed. If you use the smallest amount of space necessary to hold all the strings, your programs will suffer from repeated "garbage collection." This means that your programs will run much slower because the interpreter will have to compress the string space more frequently than if you have more than the minimal space available. Of course, you cannot allocate more space for strings than is left in your machine after the program and the non-string variables that it uses. Try allocating different amounts of string space until you reach a good compromise. A sample output is shown in Fig. 7-5.

Program 7-8. Printer Histograms

```
10 REM SAMPLE DATA FOR HISTOGRAMS FOR PRINTER OUTPUT
20 CLEAR 2000:N=RND(10):DIM C(N)
30 FOR I=1 TO N
40 C(I)=RND(30):C$(I)="BAR #"+STR$(I)
```

```
            ******************************************************
BAR # 1     ******************************************************
    24      ******************************************************
            ******************************************************

            ******
BAR # 2     ******
     3      ******
            ******

            ***********************************
BAR # 3     ***********************************
    16      ***********************************
            ***********************************

            ****
BAR # 4     ****
     2      ****
            ****

            ********************************************
BAR # 5     ********************************************
    20      ********************************************
            ********************************************

            ***********************************
BAR # 6     ***********************************
    15      ***********************************
            ***********************************

            ******************************************
BAR # 7     ******************************************
    18      ******************************************
            ******************************************

            ********************************************
BAR # 8     ********************************************
    20      ********************************************
            ********************************************
```

Fig. 7-5. Printer histogram.

```
50 NEXT I:
52 INPUT"ENTER PRINTER WIDTH";WP
60 GOSUB 1000:REM PLOT IT
70 A$=INKEY$:IF A$=" " THEN 70 ELSE IF A$<>"N" THEN CLEAR:GOTO10
80 END
1000 REM PRINTER HISTOGRAM PLOT ROUTINE
1010 REM N=NUMBER OF CATEGORIES, WP=PLOT
     WIDTH,IN=WIDTH OF INTERVAL BETWEEN BARS
1020 BW=4:REM BAR WIDTH
1022 LB=1:FOR I=1 TO N:IF LB<LEN(C$(I)) THEN LB=LEN(C$(I))
1024 NEXT I:REM MAX LENGTH OF BAR NAME
1026 WP=WP-LB
1030 MH=C(1):LH=C(1): REM FIND MAX AND MINIMUM HEIGHT
1040 FOR I=1 TO N
1050    IF C(I)>MH THEN MH=C(I)
1060    IF C(I)<LH THEN LH=C(I)
1070 NEXT I
1080 REM SC=SCALE FACTOR
1090 SC=WP/MH:ND=LEN(STR$(MH))-1:REM ND=MAX NUMBER OF
     DIGITS
1100 REM NOW PLOT IT
1110 CLS:PO=IN:UL$="%" +STRING$(LB,32)+"%": LW=(LB+2-ND)/2:IF
     LW=>0 THEN UW$=STRING$(LW,32)+
     STRING$(ND,"#")+STRING$(LW+.5,32)
1120 FOR I=1 TO N:B$=STRING$(SC*C(I),"*")
1130    LPRINT:LPRINT STRING$(LB+2,32);B$
1150    LPRINT USING UL$;C$(I);:LPRINT B$
1160    LPRINT USING UW$;C(I);:LPRINT B$
1170    LPRINT STRING$(LB+2,32);B$
1210 NEXT I
1220 RETURN
```

PIE CHARTS

The last graphical technique we will consider is the pie chart. It consists of a circle (the "pie") divided up into proportions. It is normally used with categorical data when there is a reasonably small number of categories (10 or fewer). The area of each piece of the pie corresponds to the proportion of the total that the piece represents. If category A in Fig. 7-6 is 1/8 of the total, then it occupies 1/8 of the area of the pie.

This is an example of a plot that is easier to construct using polar coordinates than sing rectilinear coordinates. Program 7-9 constructs a pie chart for the screen. The low-numbered lines are a sample routine to generate the data for the pie chart routine. The routines for drawing the pie chart are contained in line numbers above 1000. Notice that we use user-defined functions to compute the x and y

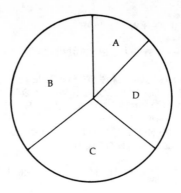

Fig. 7-6. Pie chart.

coordinates from the polar coordinates. If you lack user-defined functions, then just substitute the definition of the functions into the SET command parameters. Then, the percentages accounted for by the various categories are calculated and put into the array P(I). The points on the circumference of the circle that correspond to the end of the arc for the categories are calculated and lines are drawn to them from the circle's center. After the program is through, it goes into an infinite loop in order to preserve the screen. You must press the BREAK key to exit the program.

Program 7-9. Pie Charts

```
10 REM SAMPLE DATA ROUTINE
20 N=RND(4)+2:DIM A(N),P(N)
30 FOR I=1 TO N
40      A(I)=RND(30)
50 NEXT I
60 REM DRAW PIE CHART
70 GOSUB 1000
80 GOTO 80
999 END
1000 REM DRAW CIRCLE
1005 PI=3.14159265
1010 REM THESE FUNCTIONS DEFINE THE CIRCUMFERENCE OF THE CIR-
     CLE
1020 REM XC=CENTER OF CIRCLE, XR=X RADIUS, TH=ANGLE
1030 REM YC=CENTER OF CIRCLE, YR=Y RADIUS, TH=ANGLE
1040 DEF FN X(XC,XR,TH)=XC+XR*COS(TH)
1050 DEF FN Y(YC,YR,TH)=YC+YR*SIN(TH)
1060 XC=64;YC=24:REM (XC,YC)=CENTER OF CIRCLE
1070 XR=60:YR=20:REM X AND Y RADII
1080 CLS:FOR TH=0 TO 6.4 STEP 0.01
```

```
1090    SET(FN X(XC,XR,TH),FN Y(YC,YR,TH))
1100 NEXT TH
1110 REM DETERMINE GROUPS PERCENTAGES OF TOTAL
1120 FOR I=1 TO N
1130    TT=TT+A(I)
1140 NEXT I:REM TT=TOTAL
1150 REM P(I)=PERCENTAGE A(I) IS OF TOTAL
1160 FOR I=1 TO N
1170    P(I)=A(I)/TT
1180 NEXT I
1190 REM DETERMINE POINTS ON CIRCLE TO DRAW TO FOR ARCS
1200 TH=0:XB=XC+XR*COS(TH):YB=YC:GOSUB 1290:REM DRAW LINE
1210 FOR I=1 TO N−1
1220    TH=TH−P(I)*PI*2:REM ANGLE
1230    XB=FN X(XC,XR,TH):YB=FN Y(YC,YR,TH)
1240    REM DRAW LINES TO POINTS ON CIRCLE
1250       GOSUB 1290:REM DRAW LINE FROM (XB,YB) TO (XC,YC)
1260 NEXT I
1270 RETURN
1280 REM DRAW LINE FROM (XB,YB) TO (XC,YC)
1290 DEF FN YL(SL,IN,XP)=SL*XP+IN
1300 SX=SGN(XB−XC):IF SX=0 THEN 1380
1310 SL=(YB−YC)/(XB−XC):REM SLOPE
1320 IN=YC−SL*XC
1330 FOR X=XC TO XB STEP SX/2
1340    SET(X,FN YL(SL,IN,X))
1350 NEXT X
1360 RETURN
1370 REM VERTICAL LINE
1380 FOR Y=YB TO YC STEP SGN(YC−YB)
1390    SET(XC,Y)
1400 NEXT Y
1410 GOTO 1360
```

The pie chart program for the printer is shown in Program 7-10. It uses a somewhat different approach. It builds an array of strings and treats this array like an x,y-coordinate system. The pieces of the pie are filled in with different characters, depending on the category. The characters were chosen on the basis of visual density, so that they alternate light/heavy. For example, the first character is a period ("."), the second character is a crosshatch ("#"), and the third character is a dash ("-"). A legend, ascribing the characters used to fill in the sectors of the circle, is printed below the pie chart, in Fig. 7-7.

The number of print lines is used to determine both the width and the length of the pie chart. To make the circle look circular rather than elliptical, the width is 1.5 times the number of print lines. If you use a different font, you may wish to change this value to keep the pie looking like a pie.

There are many ways to fill in the sectors. For example, you may:

1. draw lines from one radius line terminating the sector to the previous radius line horizontally.
2. draw lines from one radius line terminating the sector to the previous radius line vertically.
3. draw radii from the circle's center to each point on the circumference in the given sector.
4. draw arcs with progressively smaller (or larger) radii.

If you use a different character for each sector, each of these methods will "fill in" the sector with that character. The approach used in

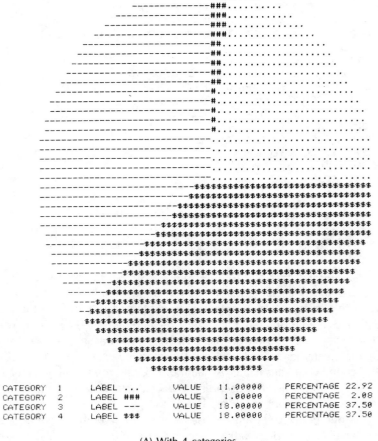

CATEGORY	1	LABEL ...	VALUE	11.00000	PERCENTAGE	22.92
CATEGORY	2	LABEL ###	VALUE	1.00000	PERCENTAGE	2.08
CATEGORY	3	LABEL ---	VALUE	18.00000	PERCENTAGE	37.50
CATEGORY	4	LABEL $$$	VALUE	18.00000	PERCENTAGE	37.50

(A) With 4 categories.

Fig. 7-7. Printer

Program 7-10 is the fourth one. The program computes the next angle bounding the sector and draws arcs for each radius length from the radius of the circle to zero. Each arc is then "filled in" with the character corresponding to the value.

As you can see in Fig. 7-7, the technique makes reasonable pie charts. The program does require several minutes to build the strings. When it is done, then it prints them out. So that you can tell that the program is still running and where it is, it prints out the current character after finishing the plot of each arc in the string array. The first section of the program is a simple driver routine that generates the data and makes the calls to the appropriate subroutines.

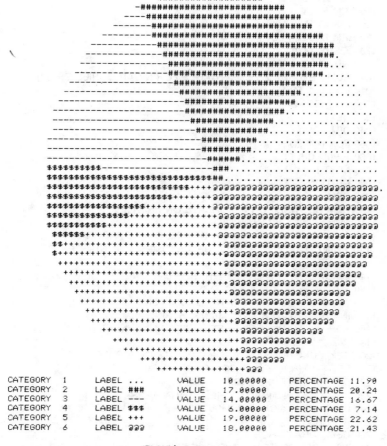

CATEGORY	1	LABEL ...	VALUE	10.00000	PERCENTAGE 11.90
CATEGORY	2	LABEL ###	VALUE	17.00000	PERCENTAGE 20.24
CATEGORY	3	LABEL ---	VALUE	14.00000	PERCENTAGE 16.67
CATEGORY	4	LABEL $$$	VALUE	6.00000	PERCENTAGE 7.14
CATEGORY	5	LABEL +++	VALUE	19.00000	PERCENTAGE 22.62
CATEGORY	6	LABEL aaa	VALUE	18.00000	PERCENTAGE 21.43

(B) With 6 categories.

pie charts.

Program 7-10. Printer Pie Charts

```
10 REM SAMPLE DRIVER PROGRAM
20 CLEAR 14000:DEFINT I
30 REM CREATE N CATEGORIES
40 N=RND(5)+2:DIM C(N)
50 FOR I=1 TO N
60     C(I)=RND(30)
70 NEXT I
80 REM GET PERCENTAGES INTO PC(I) ARRAY
90 GOSUB 1000
100 REM SET UP STRINGS
110 GOSUB 1100
120 REM DRAW LINES
130 GOSUB 1270
140 REM PLOT IT
150 GOSUB 1520
160 REM LABEL PLOT
170 GOSUB 1470
180 END
1000 REM DETERMINE PERCENTAGES FOR N CATEGORIES OF C(I)
1010 FOR I=1 TO N
1020     TT=TT+C(I)
1030 NEXT I
1040 DIM PC(N)
1050 FOR I=1 TO N
1060     P(I)=C(I)/TT
1070 NEXT I
1080 RETURN
1090 REM
1100 REM ROUTINE FOR PIE CHARTS ON PRINTER
1110 REM    SET UP STRINGS
1120 CLS:PRINT TAB(16);"HARDCOPY PIE CHART PROGRAM"
1130 PRINT"THE WIDTH WILL BE 1.5 TIMES THE NUMBER OF PRINT
     LINES"
1140 INPUT"ENTER THE NUMBER OF PRINT LINES IN PIE CHART";PL
1150 SC=1.5:REM SCALE FACTOR
1160 W=INT(PL*SC+1):RA=INT(PL/2):DIM P$(PL+2)
1170 INPUT"LEFT MARGIN";LM:LM$=STRING$(LM,32)
1180 FOR I=0 TO PL+2:P$(I)=STRING$(W+1, 32):NEXT I
1190 PI=3.14159265*2
1200 REM FUNCTIONS DETERMINE POINTS ON CIRCLE
1210 DEF FN X(R,T,OF)=(R*COS(T) +OF)*SC+1
1220 DEF FN Y(R,T,OF)=R*SIN(T)+OF+1
1230 REM C$ CONTAINS THE FILL CHARACTERS
1240 C$=". #-$+aICX="":REM ADD MORE CHARACTERS IF N>10
1250 RETURN
1260 REM    DRAW ARCS
1270 TH=0:CLS:PRINT N;" CATEGORIES":PRINT"THINKING ";
1280 FOR I=1 TO N
```

```
1290    CH$=MID$(C$,I,1):REM GET THE I-TH CHARACTER IN C$
1300    T=TH−P(I)+PI:REM TERMINATING ANGLE FOR THE ARC
1310    GOSUB 1370:REM FILL ARC
1320    TH=T:REM UPDATE ANGLE
1330 NEXT I:REM NEXT CATEGORY
1340 RETURN
1350 REM   FILL ROUTINE
1360 REM ALGORITHM IS TO FILL FROM NON-BLANK TO NEXT NON-
      BLANK
1370 REM WITH CHARACTERS
1380 FOR R=RA TO 0 STEP −.5
1390    FOR ETA=TH TO T STEP SGN(T−TH)*0.02
1400       X=FN X(R,ETA,RA)
1410       Y=FN Y(R,ETA,RA)
1420       MID$(P$(Y),X,1)=CH$
1430 NEXT ETA:PRINT CH$;:NEXT R
1440 RETURN
1450 REM   LABEL PLOT
1460 REM
1470 U$=" CATEGORY ##     LABEL % %" +
      "VALUE ####.#####     PERCENTAGE ##.##"
1480 FOR I=1 TO N
1490    LPRINT USING U$;I,STRING$(3,MID$(C$,I,1)), C(I),P(I)*100
1500 NEXT I
1510 RETURN
1520 REM PRINT IT OUT
1530 FOR I=0 TO PL+1
1540    LPRINT LM$;P$(I)
1550 NEXT I
1560 RETURN
```

REPORT WRITING

Very often it is important to have hard-copy of data in the form of reports as well as in graphs. Reports of this kind usually have a title and page number at the top of the page and maintain left, right, upper, and lower margins. When the printing would go beyond the page text length, then the printer advances to the next page and prints the title and page number, and then continues printing the data. It is difficult to write a general routine that will take care of all possible data forms, but it is fairly easy to build general routines that can quickly and easily be modified for any particular purpose.

In Program 7-11 some simple report writing routines are given. You will be prompted for the width of the report, number of physical lines per page, upper margin (which must be at least 3; the middle one being used for the title), lower margin, and left margin. The width that the printer will accept must be greater than or equal to the left margin plus the width of the report, or the report will overlap onto the next line.

The user-defined string function FN CN$(T$,W) returns a string of length L with T$ centered within it, the left margin added to it and a page number format statement right-justified in it. This string will be used in the PRINT USING statement to put the title and page number on the same line. The page number is PN, and LC is the line number. The program keeps track of the number of lines printed, so that it knows when to "page." When it is time to page, it will print the number of blank lines specified by the lower margin and the upper margin minus 2. Then the top title is printed, followed by another blank line, and the printing continues.

Program 7-11. Report Writer

```
10 REM SAMPLE DATA GENERATOR FOR REPORT WRITER
20 CLEAR 1000:N=125:M=5:DIM A(N,M)
30 FOR I=1 TO N:FOR J=1 TO M
40 A(I,J)=RND(30)+RND(0)
50 NEXT J,I
60 REM SET UP REPORT ROUTINE
70 GOSUB 1000
80 REM PRINT IT
90 GOSUB 1160
100 END
1000 REM SET UP REPORT WRITING ROUTINE
1010 INPUT"WIDTH OF REPORT";W
1020 INPUT"LEFT MARGIN";LM:LM$=STRING$(LM,32)
1030 PRINT"THE PRINTER MUST BE ABLE TO HANDLE ";LM+W;
     " CHARACTERS PER LINE"
1040 INPUT"ENTER THE TITLE OF THE REPORT";T$
1050 LT=LEN(T$)
1060 IF LT>W-10 THEN PRINT"TOO LONG!":GOTO 1040
1070 TM=3:INPUT"TOP MARGIN (MUST BE >2)";TM:TM=TM+2
1080 BM=3:INPUT"BOTTOM MARGIN (MUST BE >0)";BM
1090 PP=66:INPUT"NUMBER OF PHYSICAL LINES PER PAGE";
     PP:PL=PP-BM-TM
1100 REM FN CN$(T$,W) RETURNS T$ CENTERED IN A STRING OF
1110 REM LENGTH W WITH PAGE ## RIGHT JUSTIFIED
1120 DEF FN CN$(T$,W)=LM$+STRING$((W-8 -LEN(T$))/2,32)+
     T$-STRING$((W-8-LEN(T$))/2,32)+"PAGE ## "
1130 PG=1:INPUT"ENTER STARTING PAGE NUMBER";PG
1140 RETURN
1150 REM THIS ROUTINE ACTUALLY PRINTS THE DATA IN A(I,J)
1160 REM WITH M COLUMNS AND N ROWS
1170 REM WE WILL USE THE FORMAT ##.### FOR OUR NUMBERS
```

```
1180 U$="##.###": LU=LEN(U$):BL$=STRING$ ((W-M*LU)/(M-1),32)
1200 INPUT"PAPER READY";A$
1210 TI$=FN CN$(T$,W)
1220 REM PRINT TOP MARGIN
1230 FOR K=1 TO TN:LPRINT " ":NEXT K
1240 LPRINT USING TI$;PG:LPRINT" "
1250 LC=0:REM LC=CURRENT LINE #
1260 FOR I=1 TO N
1270 LC=LC+1
1280 IF LC<=PL THEN 1340
1290   REM IF HERE, THEN PRINT BOTTOM AND TOP MARGINS
1300   FOR K=1 TO BM:LPRINT " ":NEXT K
1310   FOR K=1 TO TN:LPRINT" ":NEXT K
1320   PG=PG+1:LC=0:LPRINT USING TI$;PG
1330   LPRINT" "
1340 LPRINT LM$;:FOR J=1 TO M
1350   LPRINT USING U$;A(I,J);:IF J<M LPRINT BL$;
1360 NEXT J
1370 LPRINT" ":REM ADVANCE TO NEXT LINE
1380 NEXT I
1390 RETURN
```

CHAPTER 8

DIFFERENTIAL EQUATIONS

A differential equation is an equation that contains one or more derivatives. The mathematical solution to a differential equation is the equation that, when differentiated, gives rise to the differential equation. That is, the function itself is unknown, but we have an equation containing one or more of its derivatives. Your job, should you choose to accept it, is to find the function that satisfies to the differential equation.

For example, if the differential equation is

$$x'(t) = \cos t, \qquad x(0)=1$$

then the analytical solution is

$$x(t) = \sin t + 1$$

The numerical solution would be to solve the differential equation above for $t=0$ to $t=a$, where a is the desired point of evaluation. In general, the differential equation is known, but the function underlying the differential equation is more difficult to come by.

There are many symbolic methods for solving differential equations. These rarely apply to numerical solutions and so will not be discussed here. In fact, many important differential equations have no analytical solutions and must be solved numerically. Rather than look at analytical methods we will instead discuss a number of ways to arrive at a numerical solution.

A numerical solution to a differential equation consists of knowing the value of the unknown function at some point or a number of points. In general, we will not be able to know the analytical definition of the function, but it may well suffice to solve it for a single value or a set of values. This is what is meant by a "numerical" solution. To arrive at a unique solution we need to know not only the differential equation, but also some particular values of the function. For first-order differential equations (equations whose highest-order derivative is 1) you need the value of the unknown function at a single point. For higher-order differential equations, things are a bit more complex.

If the values are at the same starting point for solving the system, whether it is for a single higher-order differential equation, a system of first order, or a combination of the two the problem is called an *initial value problem* (ivp). If the values are not at the same starting point, it is a *boundary value problem* (bvp), which is a more difficult numerical task. Note that for first-order differential equations, an ivp problem is the same as a bvp. For single, high-order differential equations, the ivp requirement means that the value of the functions and all derivatives up to order $n-1$ (where n is the order of the differential equation) must be known at a single point, called the initial value. For systems of first-order differential equations, the ivp requirement means that the values of all the unknown functions must be known at the same point.

There are two main approaches for the numerical solution of differential equations: Taylor series based methods, and predictor-corrector based methods. We will consider the Taylor series methods first.

TAYLOR SERIES METHODS

You will recall the definition of a Taylor series given earlier:

$$f(x+h) = f(x) + hf'(x) + \frac{h^2}{2!} f''(x) + \frac{h^3}{3!} f'''(x) + \ldots \qquad (8\text{-}1)$$

If the function $f(x)$ is analytic around x, then the Taylor series will exactly equal the value of the function at x, by definition. You can use a Taylor series to solve the differential equation for an initial value problem. The algorithm is straightforward:

1. Given the value of the function $f(x)$ at one point, x, calculate it at a short distance, h, from x: $f(x+h)$
2. Let $x+h$, and repeat step 1 until we have found the value of the function at the desired point, $f(x_p)$

Essentially, this means that given the value of the function at some point (x_0), we are going to approximate the value of the function at a point relatively far away (x_p). To do this, we take many small steps and compute the value of the function at each step. We repeat this procedure until we have reached the desired point of evaluation (x_p). This is a true example of "pulling yourself up by your bootstraps."

The Taylor series methods use the general iterative equation:

$$x_{i+1} = x_i + hg(t_i, x_i, h) \tag{8-2}$$

Since the next point, x_{i+1}, is computed in a single step, these methods are also called *one-step methods*. The predictor corrector methods use more than one step and are often called *multistep methods*. In Equation 8–2, g is called the increment function, because it tells us how to proceed from x_i to x_{i+1}.

The main problem with using the Taylor series directly is that you must be able to calculate the various derivatives $(f'(x), f''(x), f'''(x),$ and so on) of the unknown function. This means the user must spend time deriving the derivatives (if they can be easily found). Each time your applications program is run with a new problem, several equations must be entered into the program. One solution to this problem is to use numerical derivatives rather than analytical ones. However, these may be extremely inaccurate because of roundoff error.

Another problem is the same trouble we had with truncating Taylor series in the chapter on approximations. For a truncated series the Taylor series may not converge rapidly enough to the value of the function. Thus, since we are finding the value of the function at some far-away point by taking small steps and reevaluating it each time, these evaluations carry the error from previous evaluations. Hence the result may be in severe error if the Taylor series does not converge rapidly, since each term will be in error, and the error accumulates. In fact, even if the Taylor series is converging fairly quickly, if the point at which you want to approximate the function is far away, the result may be meaningless.

The standard form for a first-order differential equation is

$$x' = f(x, t) \tag{8-3}$$

where $f(x,t)$ is the (known) differential equation. In some cases, it is easy to compute the higher-order derivatives. Consider the problem

$$x' = 1 + x^2 + t^3 \tag{8-4}$$

where x is an unknown function of t. It is easy to apply the chain rule to get the derivatives for this function:

$$x'' = 2xx' + 3t^2 \qquad (8\text{-}5)$$

$$x''' = 2xx'' + 2x'^2 + 6t \qquad (8\text{-}6)$$

where x'' and x''' are the second and third derivatives of x with respect to t.

CHOOSING A STEP SIZE

A very difficult question to answer is, "What is the best step size?" If the Taylor series is rapidly converging, then a large step size may be used. If it is not, then a small step size may be better. In general, it is a good idea to use a power of 2 as a step size because the number can be represented exactly in binary form, hence without roundoff error due to representation. For example, $2^{-7} = 1/128$ may be an appropriate step size. This, however, may be impossible to perform in practice. The larger the step size, the fewer steps it will take to get to the desired point of evaluation. This decreases the opportunities for error to creep in. Usually, though, this means that each term will have more error by itself. If you use a small step size, then the error in each term will be less, but there will be more steps to be in error. Further, there will be more chances for simple errors, such as those discussed in the first chapter, to accumulate. Lastly, the time it takes to evaluate the problem will be longer. The proper step size is a function of the convergence of the Taylor series and the behavior of the function itself around the point of evaluation. If the derivatives are nearly constant, then a larger step size may be taken for a given accuracy than if the derivatives are rapidly changing.

A step size that is too small wastes time and allows roundoff error to accumulate. A step size that is too large is too inaccurate for each step. Many applications programs automatically adjust the step size according to some criterion.

The one-step methods do have the advantage that it is easy to adjust the step size. One simple method for adjusting step size is to apply some criterion to the result of a step. If the criterion says the step size was too large, then halve the step size; if the criterion says the step size was too small, then double the step size. But what is a suitable criterion?

What is needed is an estimate of the error produced in the step. When the error estimate is smaller than the accuracy desired, then you may increase the size of the step taken. When it is larger, then the step size should be decreased. We will incorporate variable step sizes in the programs that use the more popular methods. For now, just keep in mind why we might want to have a program that automatically adjusts the size of the steps it takes.

EULER'S METHOD

The simplest one-step method is called Euler's (pronounced "oilers") method. This is a Taylor series method that uses only the first term of the Taylor series and ignores the higher-order terms. The general iterative equation of Euler's method is

$$x_{i+1} = x_i + hf(x_i,t_i) \qquad (8\text{-}7)$$

Written out, this is

$$x_{i+1} = x_i + hx'(t) \qquad (8\text{-}8)$$

where x' is given by Equation 8-3.

To choose a simple step size, suppose we are starting at $x(a)$ and wish to compute the value for $x(b)$. We can then choose a fairly large n, so that $(b-a)/n$ is about the right size for the accuracy desired. We can then iterate for exactly n steps to get the answer. The value for t at the ith iteration is given by

$$t_i = a + ih \qquad (8\text{-}9)$$

since $t=a$ is the starting point.

If the differential equation is well behaved at (x_i,t_i), then our estimate should be close. It won't, in general, be exactly the same, for reasons you should know quite well by now. The estimate we compute is then used in the next step to generate the $(i+1)$st estimate. Any error already in the ith estimate will be added to the error produced in the process of the next estimation. This is called *accumulated roundoff error* because it accumulates as the iteration proceeds.

For space vehicles, on-board computers calculate the trajectories and course corrections as systems of differential equations. Rather than try to compute the exact solution (thrust, angle of thrust, etc.) for the entire trip, the system is solved only locally. Once the ship physically arrives at the local solution (the point in space-time at which the ship arrives on its course) the system is solved again, locally. This is why there are course corrections in space flight. This is done precisely to avoid the problem of severe accumulated roundoff error that might literally put you millions of miles off course.

A graphical interpretation of Euler's method is shown in Fig. 8-1. Program 8-1 shows how simple it is to code.

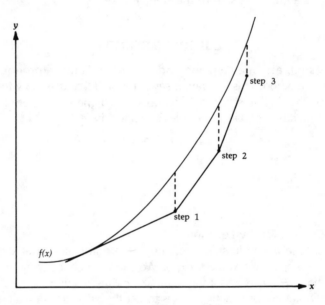

Fig. 8-1. Euler's method.

Program 8-1. Euler's Method

```
10 REM      Euler's method for differential equations
20 REM      put your differential equation in line 40
30 REM      in the form DEF FN (X,T) = . . . .
40 DEF FN F(X,T)=X↑2 + T↑3 + 2:REM sample diff eq.
50 INPUT"Enter initial point and initial value";T0,X0
60 INPUT"Enter the ending point and number of steps";TE,N
70 H=(TE−T0)/N:X=X0
80 FOR T=T0 TO TE STEP H
90    X=X+FN F(X,T)
100    PRINT"POINT T=";T;" VALUE OF X(T)=";X
110 NEXT T
120 END
```

The program requests the initial value of the unknown function $x(t)$. This is the value of $x(t)$ when t is the starting point. In the sample function given in Program 8-1, if the starting point is $t=0$, and you know the initial condition is $x(0)=0$ as the initial value, you can enter these values into the program to generate a solution to the known function at some later value of *t*. Integration of a differential equation yields a family of curves called *isoclines* that differ only by a constant. In order to determine which of this family is the appropriate one, an initial value must be given. This uniquely determines the solution.

TAYLOR SERIES METHODS OF HIGHER ORDER

If more accuracy is required per step, a method that uses more of the terms of the Taylor series may be used. To use this method you must be able to compute the higher-order derivatives of the unknown function knowing only the differential equation. This may not be possible, or even if it is, it may not be worth the effort: Program 8-2 shows a direct Taylor series method using the three derivatives of the sample differential equation given in Program 8-1.

Program 8-2. Third-Order Taylor Series Method

```
10 REM Third-order Taylor series method
20 REM put your differential equation in line 40
30 REM in the form DEF FN (X,T) = . . . .
40 DEF FN F(X,T)=X↑2 T↑3 + 2:REM sample diff eq.
50 INPUT"Enter initial point and initial value";T0,X0
60 INPUT"Enter the ending point and number of steps";TE,N
70 H=(TE-T0)/N:X=X0
80 FOR T=T0 TO TE STEP H
90   X1 = FN F(X,T)
100  X2 = 2 * X* X1 + 2 * T↑2
110  X3 = 2 * X * X2 + 2 * X1 * X1 + 6 * X2
120  X = X + H*(X1 + H/2*(X2/2 + H*X3/3))
130  PRINT"POINT T=";T;" VALUE OF X(T)=";X
140 NEXT T
150 END
```

Line 120 is the truncated Taylor series written in nested parenthetical form. The term X1 is the first derivative, generated by the differential equation, and X2 and X3 are the analytically determined second and third derivatives, respectively. These are substituted by the user into the Taylor series in line 120 to generate the estimate for X(T).

The Taylor series method, when it converges rapidly and the higher-order derivatives are easily calculated, is generally a very accurate method. However, because it is not applicable to all problems and because it involves so much user work to operate, it is not used very often. The Euler method is used for a "quick and dirty" solution, that is, when extreme accuracy is not required but speed is important. The next type of solutions, Runge-Kutta methods, are much more widely used.

RUNGE-KUTTA METHODS

The error of the Euler Method is of the order h^2 (abbreviated $O(h^2)$), where h is the size of the step used. Carl Runge and Wilhelm Kutta developed a method for solving differential equations which is called, democratically enough, the Runge-Kutta method. The Runge-Kutta method is actually a class of algorithms using an average of weighted estimates of the slope to produce a more accurate estimate of the next point. It uses more information than the Euler method and is generally preferred. The fourth-order Runge-Kutta algorithm has an error of the order h^5 ($O(h^5)$). For a small h you can see that h^5 will be much smaller than h^2. Therefore the Runge-Kutta methods incorporate less error in each step of the iterative solution at the expense of increase computation time.

Since this is a bit more advanced chapter than the preceding ones a little more mathematical expertise on the part of the reader will be assumed. Some justification (no rigorous proofs, though) for the Runge-Kutta method will actually be provided. Consider the Taylor series for a function of two variables, $f(x,y)$:

$$f(x+h, y+k) = \sum_{j=0}^{\infty} \left[\left(h\frac{\partial f}{\partial x} + k\frac{\partial f}{\partial y} \right)^j \right] \frac{1}{j} \qquad (8\text{-}10)$$

where $(\partial f/\partial x)^j$ is the jth partial derivative of $f(x,y)$ *with respect to* x. The meaning of the term in large parenthesis for $j=0$, 1, and 2 is:

$$\left(h\frac{\partial f}{\partial x} + k\frac{\partial f}{\partial y} \right)^0 = f(x,y) \qquad (8\text{-}11)$$

$$\left(h\frac{\partial f}{\partial x} + k\frac{\partial f}{\partial y} \right)^1 = h\frac{\partial f}{\partial x} + k\frac{\partial f}{\partial y} \qquad (8\text{-}12)$$

$$\left(h\frac{\partial f}{\partial x} + k\frac{\partial f}{\partial y} \right)^2 = h^2\frac{\partial^2 f}{\partial x^2} + 2hk\frac{\partial^2 f}{\partial x\partial y} + k^2\frac{\partial^2 f}{\partial y^2} \qquad (8\text{-}13)$$

where all the partial derivatives are evaluated at (x,y).

We can make the substitution of subscripts to make the notation a little more transparent. We will denote the partial derivative of $f(x,y)$ with respect to x as f_x, the second partial derivative with respect to x as f_{xx}, the second partial derivative of $f(x,y)$ with respect to x and y as f_{xy}. This enables us to rewrite Equation 8–10 as the sum of an infinite series:

$$f(x+h,y+k) = f(x,y) + (hf_x + kf_y) + \frac{1}{2!}(h^2f_{xx} + 2hkf_{xy} + k^2f_{yy})$$

$$+ \frac{1}{3!}(h^3f_{xxx} + 3h^2kf_{xxy} + 3hk^2f_{xyy} + k^3f_{yyy}) + \cdots \qquad (8\text{-}14)$$

where all partial derivatives are evaluated at (x,y). Notice that this is in the general form of a one-step method, namely,

$$f_{i+1} = f_i + g(x_i,y_i;h) \qquad (8\text{-}15)$$

The number of terms we include from the second-order Taylor series is then the correction term $g(x_i,y_i,h)$.

In order to use this method, we must be able to calculate the higher-order derivatives. From Equation 8-3, $x'=f(x,t)$, so the second derivative of $x(t)$ is given by

$$x''(t) = \frac{d(x'(x))}{dt} = \frac{\partial f}{\partial t}\frac{dt}{dt} + \frac{\partial f}{\partial x}\frac{dx}{dt} = f_t + f_xf \qquad (8\text{-}16)$$

If we take the Taylor series expansion of $x(t)$ through the second derivative term, we get:

$$x(t+h) = x(t) + hf + \frac{h^2}{2}f_t + \frac{h^2}{2}ff_x + \text{error} \qquad (8\text{-}17)$$

by virtue of Equation 8-16.

Of course, $f(x,t)$ is the differential equation we are trying to solve. The Runge-Kutta algorithm seeks a solution to the problem of finding the incremental function g of Equation 8-15 by using a series of estimates of the slope:

$$\begin{aligned}
F_1 &= hf(x,t) \\
F_2 &= hf(x+a_1F_1,t+b_1h) \\
&\;\vdots \\
F_{j+1} &= hf(x+a_jF_j,t+b_jh)
\end{aligned} \qquad (8\text{-}18)$$

A weighted average of these estimates is then used to estimate the incremental function. This is then added to the value of x_i to get the x_{i+1} term of the sequence. Let's consider the second-order Runge-Kutta method first. It uses F_1 and F_2:

$$F_1 = hf(x,t)$$

$$F_2 = hf(x+aF_1,t+bh)$$

and, so,

$$x(t+h) = x(t) + w_1F_1 + w_2F_2$$

$$x(t+h) = x(t) + (w_1 + w_2)hf + bw_2h^2f_t + aw_2h^2ff_x \quad \text{(8-19)}$$

by expanding $F_2 = hf(a+F_1, b+th)$ in a Taylor's series to the second power of h.

The next task is to get Equations 8-17 and 8-19 to agree as well as possible. One easy way to get agreement is to let

$$w_1 + w_2 = 1$$

$$aw_2 = 1/2 \quad \text{(8-20)}$$

$$bw_2 = 1/2$$

Solving the system of Equation 8–20 cannot be done unambiguously since we have one more variable than equation. This, however, gives us a *degree of freedom* to choose the answer. A convenient choice is

$$w_1 = 1/2$$

$$w_2 = 1/2$$

$$a = 1 \quad \text{(8-21)}$$

$$b = 1$$

This yields the second-order Runge-Kutta algorithm, which is shown in Chart 8-1.

Chart 8-1. Second-Order Runge-Kutta Algorithm

$$
\begin{aligned}
x(t+h) &= x(t) + (F_1 + F_2)/2 \\
F_1 &= hf(x,t) \\
F_2 &= hf(x+F_1,t+h)
\end{aligned}
\quad \text{(8-22)}
$$

This particular algorithm is rarely used, since the error term is only of order h^3. The most popular Runge-Kutta algorithm by far is the fourth-order algorithm, which has an error term $O(h^5)$. This is shown in Chart 8-2 and Fig. 8-2.

Chart 8-2. Fourth-Order Runge-Kutta Algorithm

$$
\begin{aligned}
x(t+h) &= x(t) + (F_1 + 2F_2 + 2F_3 + F_4)/6 \\
F_1 &= hf(x,t) \\
F_2 &= hf(x+F_1/2,t+h/2) \\
F_3 &= hf(x+F_2/2,t+h/2) \\
F_4 &= hf(x+F_3,t+h)
\end{aligned}
\quad \text{(8-23)}
$$

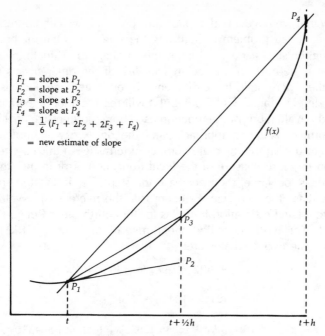

F_1 = slope at P_1
F_2 = slope at P_2
F_3 = slope at P_3
F_4 = slope at P_4
$F = \frac{1}{6}(F_1 + 2F_2 + 2F_3 + F_4)$

= new estimate of slope

Fig. 8-2. Runge-Kutta method.

The beauty of this method is that no higher-order derivatives must be calculated, yet the error term contains only terms of h^5 and above. This routine is simple to code, as is shown in Program 8-3.

Program 8-3. Fourth-Order Runge-Kutta Method

```
10 REM Fourth-order Runge-Kutta Method
20 DEF FN DY(X,Y) = X−2*X*Y:REM Diff eq. to be solved
30 H=1/128:REM default step size
40 INPUT"Enter step size";H
50 INPUT"Enter starting and terminating point";XT,XE
60 INPUT"Enter initial value of function";Y
70 H2=H/2
80 REM begin loop
90 FOR X=XT TO XE STEP H
100    F1=H*FN DY(X,Y)
110    F2=H*FN DY(X+H2,Y+F1/2)
120    F3=H*FN DY(X+H2,Y+F2/2)
130    F4=H*FN DY(X+H,Y+F3)
140    Y=Y+(F1+2*F2+ 2*F3+F4)/6
150    PRINT"Y(";X;")=";Y
160 NEXT K
170 END
```

Now that we have a real applications program, we can address the aforementioned problem of adjusting the step size. One method for adjusting the step size would be, every so often, to evaluate the next point with step size h and again with $h/2$. If the difference is very small, then increase h. If the difference is too large, then decrease h.

This simple strategy will work, but it will require a lot of extra code and eight evaluations of the function each time the step size checking is performed. Another approach, and the one we will implement here, is to use an intermediate number of terms (6, in this case) each iteration to get a measure of the local truncation error in the step. If the error is too large, then decrease the step size; if it is too small, then increase the step size. Felhberg (see the references) developed two interrelated estimation formulas for the fourth-order Runge-Kutta method. This will be called the Runge-Kutta-Felhberg (RKF) algorithm. The two estimates are:

$$y_{a,i+1} = y_i + h[(25/216)K_1 + (1408/2565)K_3$$

$$+ (2197/4104)K_4 - (1/5)K_5] \tag{8-24A}$$

$$y_{b,i+1} = y_i - h[(16/135)K_1 + (6656/12825)K_3 + (28561/564330)K_4$$

$$- (9/50)K_5 + (2/55)K_6] \tag{8-24B}$$

where
$K_1 = f(x,y)$
$K_2 = f(x+h/4,y+hK_1/4)$
$K_3 = f(x+3h/8,y+h(3K_1 + 9K_2)/32)$
$K_4 = f(x+12h/13,y+h(1932K_1 + 7200K_2 + 7296K_3)/2197)$
$K_5 = f(x+h,y+h(439K_1/216 - 8K_2 + 3680K_3/513 - 845K_4/4104))$
$K_6 = f(x+h/2,y+h(-8K_1/27 + 2K_2 - 3544K_3/2565 + 1859K_4/4104$
$$- 11K_5/40))$$

Evaluation of each of the K_is requires one evaluation of $f(x,y)$. This is the differential equation to be solved. In some instances, the function is quickly and easily evaluated. In many real-life applications, however, things are not so easy. In fact, it is not uncommon for the evaluation of the differential equation to take a major portion of the computational time. The straight fourth-order Runge-Kutta algorithm requires four evaluations of the function each iterative step. The RKF algorithm requires six per step, as shown by the system of Equations 8-24A, 8-24B, and 8-25.

Because the RKF algorithm is more involved than any other that we have dealt with, the algorithm is outlined in Chart 8-3. It is written in a pseudo-language to aid readability. The pseudo-language is similar to Pascal. A BASIC program that uses this algorithm is presented in Program 8-4.

Chart 8-3. Runge-Kutta-Fehlberg Algorithm

```
                           (RKF4)
          (Solve the system x'(t):=f(x,t), with x(Tinit):=Xinit)
                    {  **      Initialize     **  }
                       {   Get problem parameters     }
GET(Tinit, Tend, Xinit, Rmax, Min, Max, Hmin)
{   Tinit     := initial time   }
{   Tend      := ending time   }
{   Xinit     := value of unknown function at Tinit   }
{   Rmax      := accuracy control parameter   }
{   Min, Max := stepsize control parameters   }
h    := (Rmax)¼       { set initial value of h   }
Hmin := h * 10⁻⁴      { set minimum allowable step size   }
t := Tinit; x := Xend     {   set up initial values   }
                    {   **      Iterate      **   }
DO UNTIL (Termination Test = TRUE)
 BEGIN
    If t+h>Tend THEN h:=Tend − (step size for final step)
    ESTIMATE     { estimate error for next step }
    Error:= K1/360 − 128*K3/4275 − 2197*K4/75204 + K5/50 + 2*K/55
                    {   **      Accuracy Test     **   }
  Ratio := Error/h
  IF Ratio <= Rmax THEN     {   accuracy of y acceptable   }
    BEGIN
       t := t + h
       y := y + slope
    END     {   end IF accuracy acceptable   }
                    {   **Set Next Step Size ** }
  Scale := 0.84 * (Rmax/Ratio)¼
  IF Scale < Min THEN Scale := Min
  IF Scale > Max THEN Scale := Max
  h := Scale * h
                    {   ** Termination Test **   }
  IF (t=Tend) OR (h(<Hmin) THEN Termination Test := TRUE
END          {   end UNTIL statement   }
```

Program 8-4. Runge-Kutta-Fehlberg Method

```
10 REM    RUNGE-KUTTA-FEHLBERG PROGRAM IN BASIC
20 REM PUT YOUR DIFFERENTIAL EQUATION IN LINE 40
```

```
30 DEFINT I,J
40 DEF FN F(X,T)=-T*X↑2
50 REM INITIALIZE SYSTEM
60 INPUT"ENTER STARTING AND ENDING VALUES OF T";TI,TE
70 T=TI
80 INPUT"ENTER INITIAL VALUE OF F(X,T)";X
90 RM=1E-4:INPUT"ENTER RMAX":RM
100 MN=0.1:MX=4:INPUT"ENTER SCALE MINIMUM AND
    MAXIMUM";MN,MX
110 H=RM[(1/4)
120 HM=H*0.0001
130 REM SET UP COEFFICIENTS FOR EVALUATION OF THE K-S.
140 DIM A(8,6),K(6)
150 A(1,0)=0:A(1,1)=0
160 A(2,0)=1/4:A(2,1)= 1/4:A(3,0)=3/8:A(3,1) =3/32:A(3,2)=9/32
170 A(4,0)=12/13:A(4,1) =1932/2197:A(4,2)=- 7200/2197: A(4,3)=7296/2197
180 A(5,0)=1:A(5,1)= 439/216:A(5,2)= -8:A(5,3)=3680/513:
    A(5,4)=-845/4104
190 A(6,0)=1/2:A(6,1)=- 8/27:A(6,2)=2:A(6,3)=- 3544/2565:
    A(6,4)=1859/4104:A(6,5)=- 11/40
200 REM FOR ERROR ESTIMATE
210 A(7,1)=1/360:A(7,2) =0:A(7,3)=-128/4275: A(7,4)=-2197/75204:
    A(7,5)=1/50:A(7,6)=2/55
220 REM FOR COMPUTING NEXT ESTIMATE OF FUNCTION
230 A(8,1)=25/216:A(8,3) =1408/2565:A(8,4)=2197/4104: A(8,5)=-1/5
240 REM    ITERATE
250 REM TEST FOR FINAL STEP
260 IF T+H>TE THEN H=TE-T
270 REM CALCULATE THE K-S
280 FOR I=1 TO 6
290    XI=0
300    FOR J=1 TO I-1
310      XI=XI+K (J)*A(I,J)
320    NEXT J
330    K(I)=H*(FN F(X+XI,T+A(I,0)*H))
340 NEXT I
350 REM NOW, CALCULATE THE ERROR ESTIMATE, ER
360 ER=0
370 FOR J=1 TO 6
380    ER=ER+K(J) *A(7,J)
390 NEXT J
400 REM ACCURACY TEST
410 RA=ABS(ER/H)
420 IF RA>RM THEN GOTO 510
430 REM ACCURACY ACCEPTABLE
440 T=T+H
450 XI=0
460 FOR J=1 TO 5
470    XI=XI+A(8,J) *K(J)
480 NEXT J
```

```
490 X=X+XI
500 PRINT"RESULT AT T=";T;" WITH STEP H=";H;" IS ";X
510 REM ADJUST STEP SIZE
520 SC=.84* (RM/RA)↑(1/4)
530 IF SC<MN THEN SC=MN
540 IF SC>MX THEN SC=MX
550 H=H*SC
560 REM TERMINATION TEST
570 IF (T=TE) THEN 590 ELSE IF (H<HM) THEN 620
580 GOTO 260
590 REM FOUND ANSWER
600 PRINT"FOUND ANSWER! RESULT AT T=";TE;" WAS X=";X
610 END
620 PRINT"H < HMIN OCCURRED; APPARENT SINGULARITY AROUND
    T=";T
```

Several points about the algorithm should be mentioned. The variable, Error, is an estimate fo the local truncation error of the next estimate. Rmax, Min, and Max are entered by the user and they control how the step size will be allowed to vary. Rmax is the maximum error relative to the step size that is allowed in the program; 0.0001 is a value that might be appropriate. Min and Max are limits for how large or small the scaling factor is allowed to vary; 0.4 and 4.0 are useful values for these. Hmin is the minimum allowable step size. The reason for using this is that when you have an automatically self-adjusting step size, it adjusts itself on the basis of how fast the function is changing at the current point of evaluation. At a singularity, the slope often becomes infinite, such as the tangent function at $\pi/2$. As the slope becomes infinite, the self-adjusting step size will attempt to get infinitesimally small. If you have a differential equation that is behaving in this way, it should be called to your attention! Further, you will notice in the computation of K2 that t is replaced by $t+h/4$. This means that h must be large enough so that $t+h/4$ will not result in an underflow, that is, that $t+h/4 \neq t$. For $t>0$, this means that h must be large enough so that $[1+h/(4t)]>1$.

The algorithm for getting the K values was given previously in Equations 8-25. The system of equations used are given in Equations 8-24A, 8-24B, and 8-25.

The adjustment of the step size takes place in the following manner. The Ks are evaluated. These are used to create an estimate of the local truncation error. This is essentially the difference between a fourth- and a fifth-order method. Since the fifth-order method is more accurate than the fourth order, this should provide a good error estimate for the current estimate value of the function. A ratio of this error estimate and h is made and this ratio is compared with Rmax. If the ratio is less than Rmax, then the accuracy is okay: continue with the iterative step. If it fails the accuracy test, then *do not* use these K values to compute the next approximation of the function, but instead go on to adjust the step size.

A scale factor is calculated (the variable scale). If this falls outside the limits for the size of the scale factor, then it is clipped. The step size is adjusted by the scale factor. A termination test is performed. If t equals the ending value, then we are done. Or, if h<Hmin, then something is fishy, so quit. If the termination test fails, the loop continues. The DO UNTIL (condition) loop repeats the body of the loop until some condition is met. In this case, the condition is when the Boolean variable Termination Test := TRUE. If it is non-TRUE, then repeat the iteration process until it is.

This method is to be preferred over the standard Runge-Kutta method unless a certain size step is required. We will discover in the multistep predictor-corrector methods that these methods need a one-step method, such as the Runge-Kutta method, to get them going. In this case a nonadjusting step size is more appropriate.

PREDICTOR-CORRECTOR METHODS

All the algorithms for solving differential equations we have used so far require that the differential equation be evaluated several times to complete a single iterative step forward, e.g., the fourth-order Runge-Kutta algorithm requires four. For some differential equations this can be extremely time-consuming, particularly on a microcomputer running at a relatively slow clock speed (1 to 5 MHz). There is another class of methods, called the predictor-corrector methods, that only require a *single* evaluation of the differential equation during each iterative step.

The general approach of predictor-corrector methods is that the previous estimates used to generate the last few steps are combined with a new estimate to produce a prediction about the value of the next point. This is then corrected to generate a more accurate new estimate of the value of the unknown function at the current point of evaluation. That is why they are called "predictor-corrector" methods. When the evaluation of the differential equation is particularly time-consuming, the speed advantage offered by these methods can be quite significant. Generally, they are still fairly accurate and compare favorably with the Runge-Kutta methods described earlier.

One problem with these methods is that they require several points before they can be used. This is in contrast with the other methods we have discussed which require only a single value to get started. The latter are called *self-starting* methods. In an applications program that uses a predictor-corrector algorithm, a separate routine using a self-starting method must be used to generate enough data points for the predictor-corrector method to begin. One of the results of this is the fact that adjustment of the step size becomes more difficult than with the self-starting methods. We will deal with that problem a little later.

There are many strategies for predictor-corrector methods. We will mention a very popular one and develop a routine for it. A personal favorite of the author developed by Richard Hamming of Bell Laboratories will also be presented.

Assuming that we are attempting to estimate the $(i+1)$st iteration, denoted as f_{i+1}, we must have kept a number of other step values around; the ith step (f_i), the $(i-1)$th step (f_{i-1}), and so on. The exact number of values we must have depends on the specific algorithm used.

Consider the Adams-Mouton algorithm (Chart 8-4). It predicts the next value on the basis of previous values using Equation 8-26 and makes a correction with Equation 8-27. For this reason, Equation 8-26 is called the *predictor* and Equation 8-27 is called the *corrector*.

Chart 8-4. Adams-Moulton Predictor-Corrector Algorithm

Predictor: $xp = x(t) + (h/24)[55f(x(t)) - 59f(x(t-h)) + 37f(x(t-2h)) - 9f(x(t-3h))]$ (8-26)

Corrector: $x(t+h) = x(t) + (h/24)[9f(xp) + 19f(x(t)) - 5f(x(t-h)) + f(x(t-2h))]$ (8-27)

The local error at the ith step can be shown to be approximately:

$$\text{error} \approx \frac{19}{270} \frac{|x_i - xp_i|}{|x_i|} \tag{8-28}$$

You can see that in order to use Equations 8-26 and 8-27 to predict $x(t+h)$, we will have to have the values for $x(t)$, $x(t-h)$, $x(t-2h)$, and $x(t-3h)$. Once we get going, we can store these in an array, and "rotate" each new value into the array at one end and the value $x(t-4h)$ out the other end. To get started, though, we must use a self-starting method to calculate these values. If we use a fourth-order Runge-Kutta method, as in Program 8-5, we must first generate the first four values with the step size *h* before invoking the Adams-Moulton algorithm.

Program 8-5. Adams-Moulton Method

```
10 REM    ADAMS-MOULTON PREDICTOR CORRECTOR METHOD
20 REM DEFINE YOUR DIFFERENTIAL EQUATION IN LINE 40
30 DEFINT I:U$="RESULT AT T=  ###.#### IS X= ####.####"
40 DEF FN F(X,T)=- T*X*X:REM SAMPLE DIFF EQ
50 DIM F(2)
60 INPUT"ENTER STARTING, ENDING VALUES OF T";TI,TE
70 INPUT"ENTER INITIAL VALUE OF X(T)";X
80 INPUT"ENTER THE NUMBER OF STEPS";IN
90 H=(TE-TI)/IN:T =TI:SC=H/24:H2 =H/2
100 FOR I=0 TO 2
110   F(I)=FN F(X,T):REM GENERATED POINT VALUE
120   GOSUB 310:REM GENERATE INITIAL POINTS
130   PRINT USING U$;T,X
140 NEXT I
150 REM MAIN ITERATION LOOP USING ADAMS-MOULTON ALGORITHM
160 FOR I=3 TO IN-1
170   F=FN F(X,T)
180   REM PREDICTOR EQUATION
190   P=X + SC*(55*F - 59*F(2) + 37*F(1) - 9*F(0))
200   REM CORRECTOR EQUATION
210   X=X + SC*(9*FN F(P,T+H) + 19*F - 5*F(2) +F(1))
220   REM UPDATE THE ARRAY
230   F(0)=F(1)
240   F(1)=F(2)
250   F(2)=F
260   T=T+H
270   REM OUTPUT RESULTS
280   PRINT USING U$;T,X
290 NEXT I
300 END
310 REM RUNGE-KUTTA FOURTH-ORDER METHOD
320 F1=H*FN F(X,T)
330 F2=H*FN F(X+F1/2,T+H2)
340 F3=H*FN F(X+F2/2,T+H2)
350 F4=H*FN F(X+F3,T+H)
360 X=X+(F1+2 *F2+2 *F3+ F4)/6
370 T=T+H
380 RETURN
```

Another method that works quite nicely was developed by Richard Hamming, a well-known numerical analyst. His method (Chart 8-5) uses three equations rather than the standard two. There is a predictor (Equation 8-29), a modifier (Equation 8-30), and a corrector (Equation 8-31). The final answer is given by Equation 8-32.

Chart 8-5. Hamming's Predictor-Modifier-Corrector Method

Predictor: $P_i = x(t-3h) + (4h/3)[2f(x(t)) - f(x(t-h)) + 2f(x(t-2h)]$	(8-29)
Modifier: $M_i = P_i - (112/121)(P_{i-1} - C_{i-1}]$	(8-30)
Corrector: $C_i = [9x(t) - x(t-2h) + 3h(M'_i + 2f(x(t)) - f(x(t-h))]/8$	(8-31)
Final: $x(t+h) = C_i + (9/121)(P_i - C_i)$	(8-32)

Equation 8-31 uses M' rather than M. That means that we substitute M in for $x(t)$ into the differential equation to generate a value for M'.

Program 8-6. Hamming's Method

```
10 REM   HAMMINGS PREDICTOR CORRECTOR METHOD
20 REM DEFINE YOUR DIFFERENTIAL EQUATION IN LINE 40
30 DEFINT I:U$="STEP ###: " +
   "RESULT AT T=##. ##### IS X=####.#######"
40 DEF FN F(X,T)=-T *X*X:REM SAMPLE DIFF EQ
50 DIM F(2),X(2)
60 INPUT"ENTER STARTING, ENDING VALUES OF T";TI,TE
70 INPUT"ENTER INITIAL VALUE OF X(T)";X
80 INPUT"ENTER THE NUMBER OF STEPS";IN
90 H=(TE-TI) /IN:T=TI:S1=4 *H/3:S2=112/121:S3 =1/8:S4=9/121:H2 =H/2
100 FOR I=0 TO 2
110   X(I)=X
120   F(I)=FN F(X,T):REM GENERATED POINT VALUE
130   GOSUB 370:REM GENERATE INITIAL POINTS
140   PRINT USING U$;I,T,X
150 NEXT I
160 REM MAIN ITERATION LOOP USING HAMMING'S ALGORITHM
170 FOR I=3 TO IN-1
180   F=FN F(X,T)
190   REM PREDICTOR EQUATION
200   P=X(0) + S1*(2*F - F(2) + 2*F(1)
210    REM MODIFIER EQUATION
220    M=P-S2* (P0-C)
230   REM CORRECTOR EQUATION
240   C=S3*(9*X - X(1) + 3*H*(FN F(M,T+H) + 2*F - F(2)))
250   REM UPDATE PS AND QS
260   X(0)=X(1):X(1)=X (2):X(2)=X:P0=P
270   REM UPDATE X(T)
280   X=C+S4* (P-C)
290   REM UPDATE THE ARRAY
300   F(0)=F(1):F(1) =F(2):F(2)=F
310   REM UPDATE THE TIME
320   T=T+H
330   REM OUTPUT RESULTS
340   PRINT USING U$;I,T,X
350 NEXT I
360 END
```

```
370 REM RUNGE-KUTTA FOURTH-ORDER METHOD
380 F1=H*FN F(X,T)
390 F2=H*FN F(X+F1/2,T+ H2)
400 F3=H*FN F(X+F2/2,T+H2)
410 F4=H*FN F(X+F3,T+H)
420 X=X+(F1+2 *F2+2* F3+F4)/6
430 T=T+H
440 RETURN
```

ADJUSTING THE STEP SIZE FOR PREDICTOR-CORRECTOR METHODS

One of the difficulties with the predictor-corrector methods is that it is much more difficult to adjust the step size than with any of the single-step methods. The predictor-corrector methods require four (or more) equally spaced values to predict the next value. If you change the step size, then you must go back to your single-step method, such as the Runge-Kutta method, to generate more equally spaced points with the new step size, and restart the predictor-corrector method with these new values. If the function requires many changes in step size, then a single-step method may be more appropriate.

There is, though, a simple way to adjust the step size in the predictor-corrector methods. It is not as general as the step-size adjustment routine used in Program 8-4 for the Runge-Kutta-Felhberg method, but it does work. It involves halving or doubling the step size. To use the method suggested here, you must keep more information from previous computations than in either the Adams-Moulton or the Hamming routines given in Programs 8-5 and 8-6. You must save the $f(x(t-4h))$ and follow one of the two procedures.

It is relatively easy to double the step size, h. You take one more step with the current value of h to get $x(t+2h)$. Then, you can use $f(x(t-4h))$, $f(x(t-2h))$, $f(x(t))$, and $f(x(t+2h))$, adjust the step size with $h \leftarrow h \times 2$, and proceed.

Halving the step size is a little more involved. You can interpolate the values of $f(x(t-h/2))$ and $f(x(t-3h/2))$ with the following interpolation formulas:

$$f(x(t-h/2)) = [-5f(x(t-4h)) + 28f(x(t-3h)) - 70f(x(t-2h)) + 140f(x(t-h))$$

$$+ 35f(x(t))]/128 \qquad (8\text{-}33)$$

$$f(x(t-3h/2)) = [3f(x(t-4h)) - 16f(x(t-3h)) + 54f(x(t-2h)) +$$

$$24f(x(t-4h)) - f(x(t))]/64 \qquad (8\text{-}34)$$

Now, you can use $f(x(t-2h))$, $f(x(t-3h/2))$, $f(x(t-h))$, and $f(x(t-h/2))$ as your four values for the differential equation, adjust the step size with $h \leftarrow h/2$, and continue processing.

This is easy to apply to the Adams-Moulton method, but more difficult to apply to the Hammings method. The reason is that the Hammings method also requires that you keep around previous values of the unknown function, as well as its slope (given by the differential equation). One cannot circumvent this problem with keeping an array of previously determined values, since the in-between values (for halving the step size) were not computed. They can be interpolated, or the method can be restarted with the Runge-Kutta method.

If you are going to restart the solution when you change the step size, then you should use the following termination test and adjustment.

The value of the limits on the variable RATIO should be entered by the user into the variables LO and HI. If the computed value of RATIO is less than LO or greater than HI, then adjust the step size with

$$h \leftarrow h(\text{Desired/RATIO})^{\frac{1}{4}}$$

The variable RATIO is the ratio of the computed local error term divided by the step size:

$$\text{RATIO} = \text{ABS(Error/h)}$$

The error estimate is provided by the predictor-corrector equations. For the Adams-Moulton method, it is
$$\text{Error} = 19(P-C)/270$$

For Hamming's method it is

$$\text{Error} = 9(P-C)/121$$

where P and C are the predictor and corrector, respectively.

We will leave it as an exercise for the reader to implement this into the predictor-corrector routines already provided (HINT: the FOR-NEXT loop must be abandoned, since, if the step size is self-adjusting, the number of iterations required to reach the desired point of evaluation cannot be shown ahead of time. Change it to be a termination test on the value of t, similar to what was done for the Runge-Kutta-Felhberg routine).

Which to use? It depends on your application. If accuracy is your primary objective, then Runge-Kutta-Felhberg is quite good in this regard. If computation speed is more important, then a predictor-corrector method, such as the Adams-Moulton or the Hamming's method would be better. In real-time applications, or for a good quick answer, the Euler method is quite rapid, although it does have an error function $O(h^2)$. All the methods have their strengths and weaknesses, and it is up to the user to choose depending on the particular problem at hand.

SYSTEMS OF FIRST-ORDER DIFFERENTIAL EQUATIONS

Many times, if not most of the time, physical systems require more than a single differential equation to describe them. This is true whenever there is more than one variable changing in the system, for example, in flight simulation or thermodynamics.

Consider the well-known predator-prey model: If $W(t)$ is the number of wolves in the forest, and $R(t)$ is the number of rabbits, then as $W(t)$ increases, $R(t)$ will decrease. If $W(t)$ decreases, then $R(t)$ will increase. This can be written as;

$$W'(t) = aW(t) [R(t) + b]$$

$$R'(t) = cR(t) [W(t) + d]$$

for constants a, b, c, and d.

While we discuss this and other models in the following chapter on simulation, it does serve to illustrate a simple model that does generate a system of differential equations. The predator-prey model presented is a *coupled* system, since at least one of the equations has in it the other (unknown, as of yet) function.

The approach to solving a system of differential equations is a matrix analog of the procedures used to solve a single differential equation. We will consider only initial value problems (ivp's). The system may be written in matrix format:

$$X' = F(X)$$

$$X(t_{initial}) \text{ given}$$

The procedure for solving a system of equations is very analogous to solving the single system. You solve each equation in turn during each step of the iteration. Programs 8-7 and 8-8 are the Runge-Kutta-Felhberg and Adams-Moulton methods, respectively, applied to a system of differential equations.

Program 8-7. RKF Method for Systems of Differential Equations

```
10 REM    RUNGE-KUTTA-FEHLBERG FOR SYSTEMS OF EQUATIONS
15 REM          'RKFSYS'
20 DEFINT I-J,N:U1$="   X# = ###### .######"
30 U$="ENTER INITIAL VALUE OF X# (##. ###)"
40 DEF FN GRT(A,B)=- (ABS(A))ABS(B))*A- (ABS(B)=>ABS(A))*B
50 REM SELECTOR FUNCTION—SELECTS THE PROPER DIFF EQ.
60 DEF FN SEL(K,T,X1,X2,X3,X4)= -(K=1)*FN F1(T,X1,X2,X3,X4)- (K=2)*FN
   F2(T,X1,X2,X3,X4)- (K=3)*FN F3(T,X1,X2,X3,X4)- (K=4)*FN
   F4(T,X1,X2,X3,X4)
70 REM USER-DEFINED FUNCTIONS F1(X(T)), F2(X(T)), ETC
80 DEF FN F1(T,X1,X2,X3,X4)=X2
90 DEF FN F2(T,X1,X2,X3,X4)= -X1
100 DEF FN F3(T,X1,X2,X3,X4)=0
110 DEF FN F4(T,X1,X2,X3,X4)=0
120 REM INITIALIZE SYSTEM
130 INPUT"ENTER THE NUMBER OF EQUATIONS DEFINED IN PROG-
    RAM";N
140 DIM X(4),XI(4),ER(N)
150 INPUT"ENTER STARTING AND ENDING VALUES OF T";TI,TE
160 T=TI:IT=0:REM IT=# OF ITERATIONS
170 FOR J=1 TO N
180   PRINT USING U$;J,T;:INPUT X(J)
190 NEXT J
200 RM=1E-4:PRINT"ENTER RMAX (DEFAULT=";RM;")";:INPUT RM
210 MN=0.4:MX=4: PRINT"ENTER SCALE MINIMUM AND MAXIMUM (DE-
    FAULTS ";MN;MX;")";:INPUT MN,MX
220 H=RM↑(1/4)
230 HM=H*0.0001
240 REM SET UP COEFFICIENTS FOR EVALUATION OF THE K-S.
250 DIM A(8,6),K(N,6)
260 A(1,0)=0:A(1,1)=0
270 A(2,0)=1/4:A(2,1)= 1/4:A(3,0)=3/8:A(3,1) =3/32:A(3,2)= 9/32
280 A(4,0)=12/13:A(4,1)= 1932/2197:A(4,2) =-7200/2197:A(4,3) =7296/2197
290 A(5,0) =1:A(5,1)=439/216:A (5,2)=-8:A(5,3) =3680/513:A(5,4)
    =-845/4104
300 A(6,0)=1/2:A(6,1) =-8/27:A (6,2)=2:A(6,3) =-3544/2565:
    A(6,4)=1859/4104:A(6,5) =-11/40
310 REM FOR ERROR ESTIMATE
320 A(7,1)=1/360:A(7,2) =0:A(7,3)= -128/4275:
    A(7,4)=-2197/75204:A (7,5)=1/50:A(7,6)=2/55
330 REM FOR COMPUTING NEXT ESTIMATE OF FUNCTION
340 A(8,1)=25/216:A (8,3)=1408/2565:A (8,4)=2197/4104:
    A(8,5)=-1/5
350 REM      ITERATE
360 REM TEST FOR FINAL STEP
370 IF T+H>TE THEN H=TE-T
380 REM CALCULATE THE K-S
390 FOR I=1 TO 6
```

167

```
400    FOR K=1 TO N
410      XI(K)=0
420      FOR J=1 TO I-1
430        XI(K)=XI(K)+ K(K,J)*A(I,J)
440      NEXT J
450      K(K,I)=H*FN SEL(K,T+A(1,0) *H,X(1)+XI(1), X(2)+XI(2),X(3)+XI(3),
         X(4)+XI(4))
460    NEXT K
470 NEXT I
480 REM NOW, CALCULATE THE GREATEST ERROR ESTIMATE, ER
490 ER=0
500 FOR K=1 TO N
510    ER(K)=0
520    FOR I=1 TO 6
530      ER(K)=ER(K) +K(K,I)*A(7,I)
540    NEXT I
550    ER=FN GRT(ER,ER(K))
560 NEXT K
570 REM    ACCURACY TEST
580 RA=ABS(ER/H)
590 REM    REJECT STEP IF ERROR TOO LARGE
600 IF RA>RM THEN GOTO 760
610 REM    ACCURACY ACCEPTABLE
620 FOR K=1 TO N
630    XI(K)=0
640    FOR I=1 TO 5
650      XI(K)=XI(K) +A(8,I)*K(K,I)
660    NEXT I
670    X(K)=X(K)+XI(K)
680 NEXT K
690 T=T+H:IT= IT+1
700 REM    UPDATE ALL VALUES NOW
710 PRINT "ITERATION ":IT:" WITH T=";T;" AND STEP H=":H:" :"
720 FOR K=1 TO N
730    PRINT USING U1$;K,X(K)
740 NEXT K
750 REM    ADJUST STEP SIZE
760 SC=.84*(RM/RA) ↑(1/4)
770 IF SC<MN THEN SC=MN
780 IF SC>MX THEN SC=MX
790 H=H*SC
800 REM    TERMINATION TEST
810 IF (T=TE) THEN 830 ELSE IF (H<HM) THEN 890
820 GOTO 370
830 REM    FOUND ANSWER
840 PRINT TAB(10);"DONE!      RESULTS AT T=";TE;" ARE:"
850 FOR K=1 TO N
860    PRINT USING U1$;K,X(K)
870 NEXT K
880 END
```

```
890 PRINT"H < HMIN OCCURRED; APPARENT SINGULARITY AROUND
    T=";T
```

A number of points should be made about the Runge-Kutta-Felhberg program for systems of differential equations given in Program 8-7. The defined function FN SEL is a selector function. The first argument selects the user-entered function and passes the other values to it. The reason the selector functions works is based on the Boolean result of an expression such as (k=i). If k actually equals i, then a logical TRUE (−1) is returned; if not, then a zero is returned. Since the selector function is the sum of the products (k=i)*FN Fi(T,X,...), and k=i is true for only one value of i, then FN SEL returns the value of the function selected. The negative is taken, since the logical TRUE is −1.

The program is set up for four differential equations maximum (the number used is entered by the user), but this can easily be extended. Just be sure that the argument list of FN SEL and the user-entered functions are likewise extended.

The functions entered are the differential equations of the system to be solved. The program is set up to solve the two-equation system defined by:

$$x'(t) = y(t)$$

$$(8\text{-}35)$$

$$y'(t) = -x(t)$$

If you enter the initial conditions $x(0)=0$ and $y(0)=1$, then solving this system by marching t from 0 to $\pi/2$ will provide a listing of the values of $\sin t$ and $\cos t$ from 0 to $\pi/2$, the analytical solution to the problem. Since the program uses the Runge-Kutta-Felhberg algorithm, the step size is self-adjusting. You can see that generalizing the algorithm to a system of equations is straightforward.

Because this routine so intimately uses the DEF FN capability of Microsoft BASIC, it is a little more work to convert it to a subroutine-based program to work in BASICs that lack this feature. Therefore, a version of this same program that uses subroutines rather than DEF FN is provided. It is given in Program 8-8.

Program 8-8. RKFSYS for Level II BASIC

```
10 REM    RUNGE-KUTTA-FEHLBERG FOR SYSTEMS OF EQUATIONS
15 REM    RKF II SYSTEM—WILL WORK WITH TRS-80 LEVEL II
20 REM    LEVEL II VERSION (NO DEF FN USED)
30 DEFINT I−J,N:U1$="    X# = ######.######"
40 U$="ENTER INITIAL VALUE OF X# (##.###)"
```

```
50 REM    INITIALIZE SYSTEM
60 INPUT"ENTER THE NUMBER OF EQUATIONS DEFINED IN PROGRAM";N
70 DIM X(4),XI(4),F(4),ER(N)
80 INPUT"ENTER STARTING AND ENDING VALUES OF T";TI,TE
90 T=TI:IT=0:REM    IT=# OF ITERATIONS
100 FOR J=1 TO N
110    PRINT USING U$;J,T;:INPUT X(J)
120 NEXT J
130 RM=1E-4:PRINT"ENTER RMAX (DEFAULT=";RM;")";:INPUT RM
140 MN=0.4:Mx=4:PRINT "ENTER SCALE MINIMUM AND MAXIMUM (DE-
    FAULTS ";MN;MX;")";:INPUT MN,MX
150 H=RM↑(1/4)
160 HM=H*0.0001
170 REM    SET UP COEFFICIENTS FOR EVALUATION OF THE K-S.
180 DIM A(8,6),K(N,6)
190 A(1,0)=0:A(1,1)=0
200 A(2,0)=1/4:A(2,1)=1/4:A(3,0)= 3/8:A(3,1)=3/32:A(3,2)=9/32
210 A(4,0)=12/13:A(4,1)=1932/2197:A(4,2)=-7200/2197:A(4,3)=7296/2197
220 A(5,0)=1:A(5,1)= 439/216:A(5,2)=-8:A(5,3)=3680/513:A
    (5,4)=-845/4104
230 A(6,0)=1/2:A(6,1)=-8/27:A(6,2)=2:A(6,3)=-3544/2565:
    A(6,4)=1859/4104:A(6,5)=-11/40
240 REM    FOR ERROR ESTIMATE
250 A(7,1)=1/360:A(7,2)=0:A(7,3)=-128/4275:
    A(7,4)=-2197/75204:A (7,5)=1/50:A(7,6)=2/55
260 REM    FOR COMPUTING NEXT ESTIMATE OF FUNCTION
270 A(8,1)=25/216:A (8,3)=1408/2565:A(8,4)=2197/4104:A(8,5)=- 1/5
280 REM        ITERATE
290 REM    TEST FOR FINAL STEP
300 IF T+H>TE THEN H=TE-T
310 REM    CALCULATE THE K-S
320 FOR I=1 TO N
330    FOR K=1 TO N
340       XI(K)=0
350       FOR J=1 TO I-1
360          XI(K)=XI(K) +K(K,J)*A(I,J)
370       NEXT J
380       T1=T+A(I,0) *H
390       X1=X(1)+XI (1):X2=X(2) +XI(2):X3=X(3) +XI(3):X4= X(4)+XI(4)
400       GOSUB 950:REM    GET VALUES OF F1 THROUGH F4
410       K(K,I)=H *F(K)
420    NEXT K
430 NEXT I
440 REM    NOW, CALCULATE THE GREATEST ERROR ESTIMATE, ER
450 ER=0
460 FOR K=1 TO N
470    ER(K)=0
480    FOR I=1 TO 6
490       ER(K)=ER(K) +K(K,I) *A(7,I)
500    NEXT I
```

```
510   A=ER:B=ER(K)
520   GOSUB 900:REM   GET LARGEST ERROR TERM
530   ER=GR
540 NEXT K
550 REM   ACCURACY TEST
560 RA=ABS(ER/H)
570 REM   REJECT STEP IF ERROR TOO LARGE
580 IF RA>RM THEN GOTO 740
590 REM   ACCURACY ACCEPTABLE
600 FOR K=1 TO N
610   XI(K)=0
620   FOR I=1 TO 5
630     XI(K)=XI(K) +A(8,I) *K(K,I)
640   NEXT I
650   X(K)=X(K)+XI(K)
660 NEXT K
670 T=T+H:IT= IT+1
680 REM   UPDATE ALL VALUES NOW
690 PRINT "ITERATION ";IT;" WITH T=";T;" AND STEP H=";H;" :"
700 FOR K=1 TO N
710   PRINT USING U1$;K,X(K)
720 NEXT K
730 REM   ADJUST STEP SIZE
740 SC=0.84*(RM/RA) ↑(1/4)
750 IF SC<MN THEN SC=MN
760 IF SC>MX THEN SC=MX
770 H=H*SC
780 REM   TERMINATION TEST
790 IF (T=TE) THEN 810 ELSE IF (H<HM) THEN 870
800 GOTO 300
810 REM   FOUND ANSWER
820 PRINT TAB(10);"DONE!     RESULTS AT T=";TE;" ARE:"
830 FOR K=1 TO N
840   PRINT USING U1$;K,X(K)
850 NEXT K
860 END
870 PRINT"H < HMIN OCCURRED; APPARENT SINGULARITY AROUND
    T=";T
880 END
890 REM  RETURNS THE ARGUMENT LARGEST IN ABSOLUTE VALUE
900 GR=-(ABS(A) >ABS(B)) *A-(ABS(B) =>ABS(A)) *B
910 RETURN
920 REM   PLACE YOUR DIFFERENTIAL EQUATIONS HERE IN TERMS
930 REM   OF T1, X1, X2, X3, X4
940 REM   USER FUNCTIONS F1=X1'(T), F2=X2'(T), ETC
950 F(1)=COS(T1)
960 F(2)=-SIN(T1)
970 F(3)=0
980 F(4)=0
990 RETURN
```

Program 8-9 solves systems of differential equations with a generalization of the Adams-Moulton method. It does not use a self-adjusting step size, but generally operates significantly faster than the Runge-Kutta method, for reasons discussed earlier. It also uses a selector function, but it needs only to evaluate the system of differential equations once during each iteration, while the Runge-Kutta method must do it four times. A fourth-order Runge-Kutta method is used to start the program. It can be adjusted to work in BASICs without the DEF FN feature in a manner similar to the adaptation used to change Program 8-7 to Program 8-8.

Program 8-9. Adams-Moulton Method for Systems of Equations

```
10 REM    ADAMS-MOULTON PREDICTOR CORRECTOR METHOD
20 REM        FOR SYSTEMS OF EQUATIONS
30 REM          AMSYS
40 CLEAR200:DEFINT I,K:U1$="X# (##. ######) =":
   U$="               "+U1$+ "####. ######"
50 DIM K,I
60 REM    SELECTOR FUNCTION
70 DEF FN SEL(S,T,A,B,C,D)= −(S=1)*FN F1(T,A,B,C,D)− (S=2)*FN
   F2(T,A,B,C,D)−(S=3) *FN F3(T,A,B,C,D,)− (S=4)*FN F4(T,A,B,C,D)
80 REM    DEFINE YOUR DIFF. EQ. BELOW
90 REM    IN TERMS OF T, X1, X2, X3, X4
100 DEF FN F1(T,X1,X2,X3,X4)=X2
110 DEF FN F2(T,X1,X2,X3,X4)=−X1
120 DEF FN F3(T,X1,X2,X3,X4)=0
130 DEF FN F4(T,X1,X2,X3,X4)=0
140 DIM F(4,3)
150 INPUT"ENTER THE NUMBER OF EQ. IN THE SYSTEM";N
160 INPUT"ENTER STARTING, ENDING VALUES OF T";TI,TE
170 FOR K=1 TO N
180 PRINT"ENTER INITIAL VALUE OF ";:
        PRINT USING U1$;K,T;:INPUT X(K)
190 NEXT K
200 INPUT"ENTER THE NUMBER OF STEPS";IN
210 H=(TE−TI)/IN:T= TI:SC=H/24:H2 =H/2:IT=0
220 FOR I=0 TO 2
230    FOR K=1 TO N
240      F(K,I)=FN SEL(K,T,X(1),X(2),X(3),X(4):
                 REM    GENERATED POINT VALUE
250    NEXT K
260    GOSUB 550:REM    GENERATE INITIAL POINTS
265    IT=IT+1
267    PRINT TAB(16);"ITERATION STEP";IT
270 FOR K=1 TO N
280    PRINT USING U$;K,T,X(K)
290 NEXT K
```

172

```
300 NEXT I
310 REM    MAIN ITERATION LOOP USING ADAMS-MOULTON ALGORITHM
320 FOR I=3 TO IN-1
330   FOR K=1 TO N
340     F(K,3)=FN SEL(K,T,X(1),X(2),X(3),X(4))
350     REM    PREDICTOR EQUATION
360     P(K)=X(K) + SC* (55*F(K,3)- 59*F(K,2) +
              37*F(K,1) - 9*F(K,0))
370   NEXT K
380   REM    CORRECTOR EQUATION
390   FOR K=1 TO N
400     X(K)=X(K) + SC*(9*FN SEL (K,T+H,P(1),P(2),P(3),P(4)) +
              19*F(K,3) - 5*F(K,2) +F(K,1))
410   NEXT K
420   REM    UPDATE THE ARRAY
430   FOR K=1 TO N
440     F(K,0)=F(K,1)
450     F(K,1)=F(K,2)
460     F(K,2)=F(K,3)
470   NEXT K
480   T=T+H
490   REM    UPDATE ITERATION COUNTER AND OUTPUT RESULTS
492   IT=IT+1
494   PRINT TAB(16);"ITERATION STEP";IT
500   FOR K=1 TO N
510     PRINT USING U$;K,T,X(K)
520   NEXT K
530 NEXT I
540 END
550 REM RUNGE-KUTTA FOURTH-ORDER METHOD
560 FOR K=1 TO N
570   F1(K)=H*FN SEL(K,T,X(1),X(2),X(3),X(4))
580 NEXT K
590 FOR K=1 TO N
600   F2(K)=H*FN SEL(K,T+H2,X(1) +F1(1)/2,X(2)+F1(2)/2,
            X(3)+F1(3)/2,X(4)+F1(4)/2)
610 NEXT K
620 FOR K=1 TO N
630   F3(K)=H*FN SEL(K,T+H2,X(1) +F2(1)/2,X(2)+F2(2)/2,
            X(3)+F2(3)/2,X(4) +F2(4)/2)
640 NEXT K
650 FOR K=1 TO N
660   F4(K)=H*FN SEL(K,T+H,X(1) +F3(1),X(2)+F3(2),
            X(3)+F3(3),X(4) +F3(4))
670 NEXT K
680 FOR K=1 TO N
690   X(K)=X(K)+ (F1(K)+2* F2(K)+2*F3(K) +F4(K))/6
700 NEXT K
710 T=T+H
720 RETURN
```

HIGHER-ORDER DIFFERENTIAL EQUATIONS

These three programs, Programs 8-7, 8-8, and 8-9, can be used to solve coupled or uncoupled systems of first-order differential equations. We have not touched on the problem of higher-order differential equations. Second-order differential equations are even more common than first-order, after all.

It turns out that these equations are simple to solve with the methods we have discussed for systems of equations. A differential equation of order n can be written as

$$y^{(n)} = f(t, y, y', y'', y''', \ldots) \qquad (8\text{-}36)$$

with the initial conditions

$$y(t_0) = y_0, \quad y'(t_0) = y'_0, \quad y''(t_0) = y''_0, \quad \ldots$$

Since it is an initial value problem, the values of y, y', up to the $(n-1)$st derivative of y are all known at a single initial point, t_0. If this is not the case, then you have a boundary value problem, which we will discuss briefly at the end of this chapter.

The approach commonly used for higher-order differential equations is to rewrite the single equation as a system of coupled first-order differential equations. This can be done by creating dummy variables.

Given the system in Equation 8-36, we will define the state variable y_i as the $(i-1)$st derivative of y. Applying this recursive definition, Equation 8-36 becomes:

$$
\begin{aligned}
y_1 &= y \\
y_2 &= y' \\
y_3 &= y'' \\
&\ \vdots \\
y_{n-1} &= y^{(n-2)} \\
y_n &= y^{(n-1)}
\end{aligned}
$$

This gives the system of equations:

$$
\begin{array}{ll}
y_1' = y_2 & y_1(t_0) = y_0 \\[4pt]
y_2' = y_3 & y_2(t_0) = y_0' \\[4pt]
\quad \vdots & \quad \vdots \\[4pt]
y_{n-1}' = y_n & y_{n-1}(t_0) = y_0^n \\[4pt]
y_n' = f(t, y, y', y'', y''', \ldots)
\end{array}
\qquad (8\text{-}37)
$$

This system is of the standard form for ivp's (initial value problems) and so can be solved by any algorithm that solves a system of differential equations.

Let's consider a specific example of changing an nth-order ivp into a system of n first-order ivp's. Equation 8-38 is third-order differential equation with initial value conditions.

Sample Third-Order IVP

$$x''' + tx' + xx''/t = 2e^{-3t} \qquad (8\text{-}38)$$

with

$$x(1) = -2, \quad x'(1)=1, \quad x''(1)=0$$

The first step is to solve the system for the highest derivative, $x'''(t)$:

$$x''' = 2e^{-3t} - tx' - xx''/t \qquad (8\text{-}39)$$

Let $x_1=x$, $x_2=x'$, and $x_3=x''$. This gives changes the third-order differential equation of Equation 8-38 into the system of ivp equations:

System of IVP Equations

$$F1 = x_1' = x_2 \qquad\qquad x_1(1) = -2$$

$$F2 = x_2' = x_3 \qquad\qquad x_2(1) = 1 \qquad (8\text{-}40)$$

$$F3 = x_3' = 2e^{-3t} - tx_2 - x_1 x_3/t \qquad x_2(1) = 1$$

This is coded into a BASIC program as:

```
20 DEF FN F1(T,X1,X2,X3) = X2
30 DEF FN F2(T,X1,X2,X3) = X3
40 DEF FN F3(T,X1,X2,X3) = EXP(-3*T)-T*X2 - X1*X3/T
```

The selector function used in the applications programs presented in this chapter for systems of differential equations will choose the appropriate function to evaluate. Study the conversion of the third-order ivp into the system of three differential equations and their ultimate coding in BASIC. It is the key to using this method. The process is summarized in Table 8-1.

BOUNDARY VALUE PROBLEMS

So far, we have only considered initial value problems. These are relatively easy to solve primarily because we have several pieces of

Table 8-1. Changing an IVP of order *n* into *n* IVPs

Old Variable	New Variable	Initial Value	Differential Equation
x	X1	-2	X1$'$=X2
x'	X2	1	X2$'$=X3
x''	X3	0	X3$'$=F(t,X)

where $F(t,X) = 2e^{-t} - tx' - xx''/t$

information about the function (namely, its value and the value of its $n-1$ derivatives) at the same point. We use both of these pieces of information to pull ourselves along and solve the system.

What happens when you instead know the value of the function at two distinct points? This provides information on the boundaries of a function, hence the name boundary value problem (bvp). A typical bvp is:

$$x'' = f(t,x,x') \tag{8-41}$$

with $x(a) = \alpha$ and $x(b) = \beta$.

One way to go about solving Equation 8-41 is to guess at $x'(a)$ and solve it like an ivp from $t=a$ to $t=b$ and compare the computed solution at $x(b)$ with the given value, β. If it is not the same (as will generally be the case on the first try), then change your estimate of $x'(a)$ and repeat the procedure. You repeat this procedure until you hit the correct answer for $x(b)$. This is the algorithm we will discuss here, and it is called the "shooting" method. A natural first guess is the slope of the line between (a,α) and (b,β), which is $(\beta-\alpha)/(b-a)$.

Using the shooting method, all things are kept the same during each trial except the value of $x'(a)$. If we create a variable, say z, such that $x'(a)=z$, then $x(b)$ is a function of z. We will call this function $s(z)$. The shooting method adjusts z until $s(z)=\beta$. We can compute $s(z)$, but it is expensive to do so, since an entire ivp must be solved to find it.

The value of $s(z)-\beta$ is the error of the estimate. The shooting method reduces to the finding the zero of ER(z), where $ER(z)=s(z)-\beta$. The Newton-Raphson method is rapidly converging but not particularly applicable, since we will not always be able to come up with the derivative. We can, however, use a secant method, whose iterative equation becomes

$$x_{i+1} = x_i - \frac{ER(x_i)\,(x_i - x_{i-1})}{ER(x_i) - ER(x_{i-1})} \tag{8-42}$$

Program 8-10 uses the shooting method to solve a second-order bvp with initial conditions $x(a)=\alpha$ and $x(b)=\beta$. It solves the ivp's using the Adams-Moulton predictor-corrector program (Program 8-9), but any accurate ivp system solver could have been used.

Program 8-10. Shooting Method

```
10 REM    SHOOTING METHOD FOR BOUNDARY VALUE PROBLEMS
20 CLEAR 200:DEFINT I,N:U$="X#= ####.#### ":
   U1$="ITERATION ## AT T=###.######"
30 REM    SELECTOR FUNCTION
40 DEF FN SEL(S,T,X1,X2)=-(S=1)*FN F1(T,X1,X2)-(S=2)*FN F2(T,X1,X2)
50 REM    SAMPLE BVP X"= 2X'/T; X(1)=-1; X(2)=0
60 REM    ANALYTICAL SOLUTION IS X'(T)=(T-X)/T
70 REM    ANALYTICALLY DETERMINED X'(A)=2
80 REM    X(1) RETURNS THE VALUE FROM THE AMSYS ROUTINE
90 DEF FN F1(T,X1,X2)=X2
100 DEF FN F2(T,X1,X2)=-2*X1/T
110 DIM F(2,4),X(2),F1(2),F2(2),F3(2),F4(2)
120 INPUT"ENTER FIRST BOUNDARY    T=";T1
130 INPUT"ENTER KNOWN VALUE X(A)=";XA
140 INPUT"ENTER SECOND BOUNDARY    B=";TE
150 INPUT"ENTER KNOWN VALUE X(B)=";XB
160 INPUT"NUMBER OF DIGITS OF ACCURACY";ND
170 RT=10↑(-ND)/2
180 REM    USE NUMBER OF STEPS IN METHOD
190 IN=100:INPUT"ENTER THE NUMBER OF STEPS TO USE EACH
    ITERATION";IN
200 INPUT"MAXIMUM NUMBER OF ITERATIONS";MI
210 REM    FIRST ESTIMATE OF SLOPE
220 XP=(XB-XA)/(TE-TI):XR=XP
230 REM    GENERATE AN INITIAL SOLUTION
240 GOSUB 510
250 REM    GET ERROR FUNCTION
260 EP=YB-XB
270 REM    NEXT ESTIMATE OF THE VALUE
280 XR=XP-0.2 *SGN(EP):DX=10000
290 REM    **** ITERATE    ****
300 FOR J=1 TO MI
310   IF ABS(DX)<=RT *ABS(XR) THEN 440
320   REM    SOLVE SYSTEM
330   GOSUB 510
340   ER=YB-XB
350   DX=-ER *(XR-XP)/ (ER-EP)
360   REM    UPDATE PARAMETERS
370   XP=XR:EP=ER:XR=XR+DX
380   PRINT TAB(16)"ITERATION NUMBER";J
390   PRINT TAB(16);"ERROR IS ";ER
400   PRINT"CURRENT ESTIMATE OF SLOPE AT";TI;" IS ";XR
410 NEXT J
```

```
420 PRINT"DID NOT CONVERGE"
430 END
440 REM    CONVERGENCE ACHIEVED
450 REM    TURN ON PRINT FLAG
460 FL=-1
470 REM    SOLVE SYSTEM WITH NEW VALUE FOR XR
480 GOSUB 510
490 END
500 REM    ****    AMSYS ROUTINE    ****
510 H=(TE-TI)/IN:T=TI: SC=H/24:H2=H/2:IT=0
520 X(1)=XA:REM    X(A)=XA      (GIVEN)
530 X(2)=XR:REM    X(A)=XR   (ESTIMATED)
540 FOR I=0 TO 2
550   FOR K=1 TO N
560     F(K,I)=FN SEL(K,T,X(1),X(2)):
            REM    GENERATED POINT VALUE
570   NEXT K
580   GOSUB 940:REM    GENERATE INITIAL POINTS
590   IF NOT(FL) THEN 650
600   IT=IT+1
610   PRINT TAB(10);:PRINT USING U1$;It,T
620 FOR K=1 TO N
630   PRINT TAB(20);:PRINT USING U$;K,X(K)
640 NEXT K
650 NEXT I
660 REM        MAIN ITERATION LOOP
        USING ADAMS-MOULTON ALGORITHM
670 FOR I=3 TO IN-1
680   FOR K=1 TO N
690     F(K,3)=FN SEL(K,T,X(1),X(2))
700     REM    PREDICTOR EQUATION
710     P(K)=X(K) + SC*(55 *F(K,3)- 59*F(K,2) + 37*F(K,1) - 9*F(K,0))
720   NEXT K
730   REM    CORRECTOR EQUATION
740   FOR K=1 TO N
750     X(K)=X(K) + SC*(9*FN SEL(K,T+H, P(1),P(2)) + 19*F(K,3) - 5*F(K,2)
        +F(K,1))
760   NEXT K
770   REM    UPDATE THE ARRAY
780   FOR K=1 TO N
790     F(K,0)=F(K,1)
800     F(K,1)=F(K,2)
810     F(K,2)=F(K,3)
820   NEXT K
830   T=T+H
840   REM    OUTPUT RESULTS
850   IF NOT(FL) THEN 910
860   IT=IT+1
870   PRINT TAB(10);:PRINT USING U1$;IT,T
880   FOR K=1 TO N
```

```
890      PRINT TAB(20);:PRINT USING U$;K,X(K)
900   NEXT K
910 NEXT I
920 YB=X(1)
930 RETURN
940 REM RUNGE-KUTTA FOURTH-ORDER METHOD
950 FOR K=1 TO N
960   F1(K)=H*FN SEL(K,T,X(1),X(2))
970 FOR K=1 TO N
980   F2(K)=H*FN SEL(K,T+H2, X(1)+F1(1)/2,X(2) +F1(2)/2)
990 NEXT K
1000 FOR K=1 TO N
1010   F3(K)=H*FN SEL(K,T+H2, X(1)+F2(1)/2,X(2)+ F2(2)/2)
1020 NEXT K
1030 FOR K=1 TO N
1040   F4(K)=H*FN SEL(K,T+H,X(1) +F3(1),X(2)+F3(2))
1050 NEXT K
1060 FOR K=1 TO N
1070   X(K)=X(K)+(F1(K) +2*F2(K) +2*F3(K)+F4(K))/6
1080 NEXT K
1090 T=T+H
1100 RETURN
```

A simple example of a boundary value problem is the problem:

$$x''(t) = -x(t) \qquad (8\text{-}43)$$

with $x(0)=1$ and $x(\pi/2)=2$.

The analytical solution is $x(t)=1+sin\ t$. To put this problem into the program, you must first change it into a system of first-order differential equations as shown Table 8-2. This translates into the BASIC code:

```
DEF FN F1(T,X1,X2) = X2
DEF FN F2(T,X1,X2) = -X1
```

Table 8-2. Setting up a BVP

Old Variable	New Variable	Differential Equation
x'	X1	$X1' = X2$
x''	X2	$X2' = -X1$

When the program is run, it will prompt for the first point and the value of the function at that point (in this case, 0 and 1), and the second point and the function's value at it ($\pi/2$ and 2). The program will then make estimates of $x'(0)$. These estimates will be refined until a good estimate is made (the actual slope is 1 at $x(0)$). Once the slope has been found with some accuracy, **the program will solve** this system like an ivp system.

This method is not without problems. It is a slow program, because it must solve many ivp systems before it finds a good value for the slope at the initial point. If the slope has even a small error, this can cause relatively large errors in the evaluated points. On the other hand, the method is conceptually simple and easy to program. There are many other methods for solving boundary value problems, and interested readers may investigate the topic by consulting the references.

CHAPTER 9

SIMULATION OF DYNAMIC SYSTEMS

Simulation specifically refers to marching a mathematical model through its paces. A *model* is an abstract representation of an entity or system. A model reproduces only the essential characteristics of a system. This is a very important point. A model is a simplified abstraction of a concrete entity. If it reproduced *all* the characteristics of the entity, then it would be a copy, not a model. Modelling always involves making simplifying assumptions, and these may or may not be valid. One hopes that only inessential features are omitted from the model and that the important features are represented accurately.

Models can be of any type. A clay representation of an architectural structure is a model, preserving spatial characteristics, but not their absolute dimension, nor the true material composition. The specific kind of modelling we will deal with here is mathematical modelling, the kind amenable to simulation. A concrete entity is reduced to a simplified abstraction whose features are mathematically described, i.e., they are described by mathematical equations. We will limit ourselves even further and consider only dynamic models, that is, models that change with time and so can be modelled with differential and state equations.

A *state* equation is an equation that describes the status of a system variable without the use of derivatives. A *differential* equation, such as those in the previous chapter, is an equation describing the rate of change or the rate of change of the rate of change (the second derivative), etc., of a state variable. Consider the predator-prey model briefly discussed in the last chapter.

There are wolves and rabbits in the forest—all other animals in the ecosphere are removed for simplicity. We will also assume that the prey always can find enough Purina Rabbit Chow, and the birth rate of the rabbits is proportional to the number of rabbits currently alive. The death rate is proportional to the number of rabbits *and* the number of wolves. This means that the birth rate is $ar(t)$, and the death rate is $br(t)w(t)$. The rate of change of the number of rabbits is the difference between the birth and death rates, or

$$r'(t) = ar(t) - br(t)w(t) \qquad (9\text{-}1)$$

with constants a and b.

The birth rate of the predator depends on food supply (our finely hare-d friends) and the number of predators available for procreation. Therefore the predator birth rate is $cr(t)w(t)$. The predator rate we will take as proportional to the number of predators alive at the time, or $dw(t)$. Therefore, the rate of change of the number of wolves in the forest is

$$w'(t) = cr(t)w(t) - dw(t) \qquad (9\text{-}2)$$

with constants c and d.

These two equations model the populations of the wolves and the rabbits in the ecosystem. The constants a, b, c, and d may be determined in a number of ways. A naturally occurring or artificially constructed ecosystem of this type can be observed and the constants can be determined from this. Or, if a certain theory predicts that if the constants have certain values, then certain results will happen. This is an example of using a model to test a theory. Or, you can do a "what if?" problem with these constants and observe the results.

WHY MODEL?

Some people ask the question, "Why model?" There are several possible answers to this question. First, one can argue that many experiments are costly, technically difficult, or morally impossible to perform. What happens in a runaway nuclear reactor? The results of that question determine safety precautions and are vitally important, but it is not an experiment that one would like to see performed. It is often much cheaper to simulate a system than to actually gather the data. If it can be shown that the model accurately represents the important aspects of the system under study, then it is easy to simulate a variety of conditions much more cheaply than the experiments can actually be performed, in less time, and with much greater safety.

What happens in severe hypotensive shock resulting from massive blood loss? You won't get many volunteers for that experiment! True, you can use animals to simulate humans, but animals often differ drastically in their responses. If you have a good model of the blood pressure and circulation system, you can do at least preliminary simulation studies of the effects of certain drugs with different response times to cause arterial constriction, raising the blood pressure.

Mathematical models of human thermoregulation performed by and for NASA aided in the construction of efficient space suits. Bioengineers, simulating stress patterns during strenuous activity, have been able to design better athletic shoes that support and protect the feet and legs of athletes. And in at least one lab, computer modelling of human locomotion has led to the significant result of total parapalegics and quadrapalegics being able to ride bicycles and even walk *even though they have no direct voluntary control over their leg muscles*—this is done through computer simulation of the nerve and muscle activity during locomotion producing programs that can actually be used to electrically stimulate the leg muscles in the proper amounts and sequences to produce real movement. With all these important examples, one can see the scope and importance of simulation and modelling. But there is an even more fundamental reason why modelling is important.

It has to do with human cognition. The human being, as a sentient creature, can think. All thinking is ultimately composed of interactive models of the world. Mathematics itself is a numerical model of the world that has been developed over thousands of years of civilization. What does addition mean? What concretes does it represent? It represents the concretes of grouping of physical entities, but it is itself an abstraction. Taking one apple (or TRS-80) and throwing it in with another means you have two apples. That is an example of the physical concretes that the abstraction "addition" represents. There are people (unfortunately, some of them are even university professors) who proclaim that mathematics is completely arbitrary and has nothing to do with the real world. They are dead wrong. An abstraction does not necessarily have to model the real world, even if it is supposed to, but try to imagine substituting some other mathematical manipulation for addition, and you can see that chaos will quickly result. One can only assume that this was the joke when the Tennessee legislature voted on whether or not to force the value of π to be an even 3.0.

While it is possible to conceive of mathematical constructs that have little, if anything, to do with reality, the vast majority of mathematics is a direct abstraction of the physical laws and identities that actually exist. If they weren't accurate, I dare say we would never have survived this long!

You can see, then, that there are two primary reasons for modelling. First, it is an efficient and useful tool for studying the world. Secondly, and even more importantly, our entire conceptual structure is built up of a hierarchical structure of models about the world, so we model whether we like it or not—that is the mode of human cognition.

Having given somewhat of a brief pragmatic and epistemological justification for modelling and simulation, let us now discuss the dynamic mathematical models a bit more.

MODEL OF RADIOACTIVE DECAY

A simple model to consider is the decay of a radioactive substance. The rate of decay is proportional to the amount of the substance. The same principle is true for other systems, such as the removal of a drug from the body. The equation describing this behavior is

$$x'(t) = ax \tag{9-3}$$

where a is called the proportionality constant and is a positive value. Suppose you have this differential equation and you know that $a=0.01$. If $x(0) = 1$ kg, then how much radioactive material is left after 60 minutes? Two hours? One week?

The way to solve this problem (unless you can already figure out the analytical solution to this simple problem) is to use one of the previously developed differential equation solving programs and numerically solve it. Any method will work, such as the Euler, Taylor series, Runge-Kutta, or predictor-corrector methods. They can be used to simulate the model. Remember, Equation 9-3 is the model, and the process of solving the model is called "simulation." If you plot the values resulting from the integration of the differential equation 9-3, you see something like Fig. 9-1.

THERMOREGULATORY MODEL

A slightly more complex model is presented in Fig. 9-2 and Equation 9-4, given below. It is a model of thermoregulation in a limb. The limb is idealized to be a set of three concentric cylinders corresponding to the layers skin, muscle, and core. Heat loss takes place

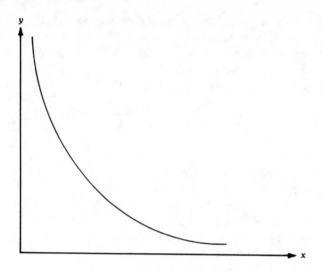

Fig. 9-1. Solution to $x'(t) = -ax(t)$.

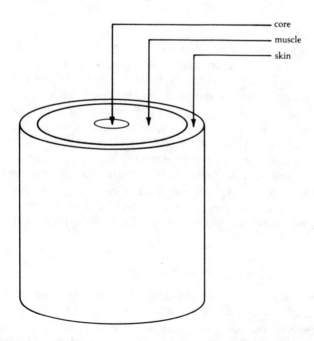

Fig. 9-2. Tissue layers for a limb thermoregulatory model.

from the core to the muscle, from the muscle to the skin, and ultimately, from the skin to the environment. The heat loss is the change in temperature with respect to time integrated over time.

If we focus just on the muscle layer for now, the model for heat flow in this layer is given in Equation 9-4:

$$CMT_m'(t) = S_m + E_m + \frac{aA_{cm}\,(T_c - T_m)}{L_{cm}} + \frac{aA_{ms}\,(T_m - T_s)}{L_{ms}} \qquad (9\text{-}4)$$

where
C = specific heat of the tissue,
M = mass of the muscle,
T_m = temperature of the muscle,
T_c = temperature of the core,
T_s = temperature of the skin,
A_{cm} = area between core and muscle,
A_{ms} = area between muscle and skin,
L_{cm} = length along the segment core to muscle,
L_{ms} = length along the segment muscle to skin,
S_m = shivering metabolism,
E_m = exercise metabolism,
a = constant.

This equation models the temperature of the muscle layer. It receives heat passively from the core layer and actively from the two forms of metabolism, shivering and exercise. See Fig. 9-3. The amount of heat that the tissue contains is the product of the mass of the tissue (M) and the specific heat of the tissue. This times the rate of temperature change is the rate of heat loss or gain. Equation 9-4 is a simple first-order differential equation for modelling the heat flow in living tissue. It is not unlike some of the papers published in models of human thermoregulation by NASA scientists; of course, it is much simpler. To make the model simple, you can assume constant amount of shivering and exercise, or you can make the model more interesting by treating the metabolic heat output of shivering as a function of temperature.

UFO MODEL

Modelling is not strictly the domain of physiologists, of course. Let's launch us a UFO. If x is the horizontal and y is the vertical coordinate of our ship, we can describe the UFO's position by second-order differential equations. To make it interesting, our UFO

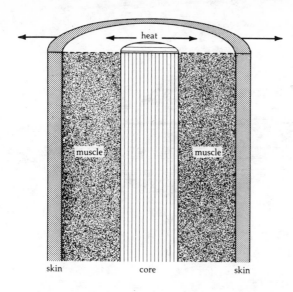

Fig. 9-3. Heat flow in a thermoregulatory model.

has two jets: one situated on the underside of the always-vertical UFO, and one on one side, providing thrust for horizontal movement. Our UFO is shown in Fig. 9-4. Since the jets are providing force ($F=ma$, after all), the second derivative of the position is proportional to the force:

$$x''(t) = \frac{\text{jet 1}}{m}$$

$$y''(t) = g - \frac{\text{jet 2}}{m} \qquad (9\text{-}5)$$

To solve this system, you must create four first-order differential equations from this system of two second-order equations, and apply one of the methods discussed in the previous chapter for solving systems of differential equations.

FEEDBACK

If the output of a system affects the system, then the system is said to recèive *feedback* or be a *closed loop system*. If the system does not receive this information back, then it is called an *open loop system*. If an increase in the output of the system causes a decrease in future outputs, it is called *negative feedback;* if an increase in the output

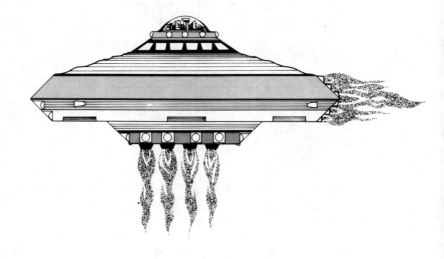

Fig. 9-4. UFO model.

causes further increase in the system, then it is called *positive feedback*. In control applications, an open loop system sends an output in response to a stimulus, but it does not check to see if it was accomplished. Well-learned motor skills are executed in an open loop fashion. When you are swinging a baseball bat, there is no time for proprioceptive feedback from nerve and sensory tracts to affect the motion. Once it is fully begun, the body cannot control the motion, because of the time factor. Learning a motor skill is done by refining a skill and, to a large degree, creating skill patterns that do not require feedback to work. The creating of feedback-independent motor patterns heavily involves the use of feedback, both positive and negative. Positive feedback might be that if a student enjoys a sport, s/he will do it more often than otherwise. This means that s/he will enjoy it more, and so s/he will do it even still more, etc. Positive feedback is sometimes called a *vicious cycle*, because, if unchecked, will cause problems. Negative feedback in motor learning is exemplified by the fact that, mostly, motor learning is the inhibition of unwanted movements. As your skill improves, fewer muscles (only the correct ones) are used.

The prototypical example of negative feedback is a temperature regulator controlling a heating system. If the temperature rises above a point, the heat is shut off. If the temperature falls, then the heater is turned on. The output of the heating system is heat (big surprise, huh). Since heat itself is the signal to stop outputting heat, this is a classic case of negative feedback.

Physiology is full of negative feedback examples in homeostatic regulation mechanisms, from thirst to temperature regulation by the hypothalamus to regulation of hormone levels. There are no true examples of positive feedback in the healthy body, because this would lead to the rapid demise of the individual. There are examples of limited positive feedback, such as the initiation of nerve impulses in the bioelectric membrane of the perikaryon, or nerve cell body. The nerve cell maintains an electrical potential through the use of molecular pumps in the membrane that move ions (mostly sodium, potassium, calcium, and chloride) across it. The membrane contains tiny pores that allow the ions to leak back in, but the pumps move them out as fast as they leak in. The pores have potential sensitive "gates" on them. In response to a drastic change in membrane voltage potential, these gates open and increase the flow of ions by hundreds of times. This causes the potential to become more positive. The more the ions flow, the more positive the potential becomes, the more the gates open and, therefore, the easier the ions flow. In a nearby section of membrane tissue this effect is felt by a change in the local potential field, and this causes the gates to open, thereby causing rapid flow of ions, causing the gates to open more, inducing more ions flow, etc. This is an example of positive feedback. The more the ions flow, the easier it becomes for the ions to flow. Luckily, though, these gates are time dependent. After a few hundred microseconds, they will close tightly and refuse to open regardless of the membrane potential. This allows the molecular pumps to get busy and restore the ion balance to the membrane, and the resting state of the membrane is restored. The only reason that this positive feedback does not kill us is that it is controlled. Uncontrolled positive feedback is always fatal.

One example of pathological positive feedback occurs in heart failure. Heart failure is the inability of the heart to pump enough blood to meet the demands of the metabolizing tissues. As the heart begins to fail, the arteries supplying the heart also begin to fail, meaning that the blood the heart itself is receiving is inadequate to meet its own demands. Of course, the heart becomes ischemic (oxygen-starved), and its ability to pump blood is reduced. Well, if it was failing before, now it is *really* failing. The result? The heart can pump even less blood. Eventually the heart up and quits.

Feedback is crucial to the proper operation of most control systems. True, there are some open loop systems, but these cannot be finely tuned to adjust the system to a state. In a negative feedback system the acuity of the control is called the *gain*. If the temperature in a room jumps from 60 to 110 degrees, but a person's body temperature rises only 1 degree in response to the increase in room temperature, then the room changes temperature by 49 degrees more than the body. If the body were not alive, its temperature would follow that of the room, but because there is active regulation, the increase in only 1 degree. The gain of this control system is −49. This means that for each unit change in body temperature, the environment must have changed by 49 times this much. Some of the regulation systems in the body, such as fluid and electrolyte regulation by the kidney, have infinite gain. This means that the system is capable of restoring itself to a certain level exactly, following a change.

HORMONAL REGULATION MODEL

Fig. 9-5 shows a hormonal regulation system that uses negative feedback. The hormone that is being regulated is thyroxine (T_4) and it is released by the thyroid gland in response to another hormone TSH, thyrotropin stimulating hormone. Actually, there is another related hormone released by the thyroid gland as well—triiodothyronine (T_3). Both T_4 and T_3 have similar effects, and the differences need not concern us here. The effect of T_4 and T_3 is to increase the basal metabolic rate (BMR), that is, the amount of energy used at rest.

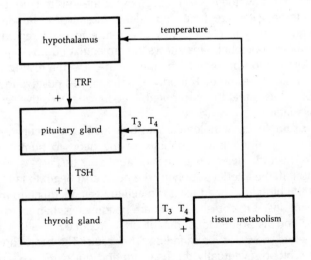

Fig. 9-5. Thyroid stimulating hormone (TSH) model.

Hormones T_4 and T_3 bind reversibly to proteins in the blood, and "piggyback" around on them. It is only the T_4 and T_3 fraction that is not bound that has any effect. The protein-bound thyroid hormones serve as a blood-based reservoir for the free-fraction T_4 and T_3. The free T_4 and T_3 cause the pituitary gland to decrease the amount of TSH it releases, so the thyroid gland doesn't produce as much T_4 and T_3. Thyrotropin releasing factor (TRF) is released by an area of the brain called the hypothalamus. The TRF stimulates the pituitary gland to release TSH.

Before we get into the mathematics, why do you think this system exists? Hint 1: one of the main purposes of the hypothalamus is the regulation of temperature. Hint 2: the hypothalamus releases TRF in response to a lowered temperature of the blood passing through it.

You guessed! If you increase the BMR, then the amount of heat produced at rest is also increased, thus increasing body temperature. If the hypothalamus senses a lowered temperature, then it increases its release of TRF. The TRF increases the amount of TSH released by the pituitary gland. The TSH stimulates all known functions of the thyroid gland, including the release of the T_4 and T_3. The T_4 and T_3 hitch a ride to the various tissues and increase their oxygen consumption and, thereby, the BMR. This increases the temperature, causing the hypothalamus to decrease the amount of TRF release, decreasing the TSH released, decreasing the T_4 and T_3, etc. Not only does the T_4-induced temperature eventually cause a decrease in the T_4 release, but T_4 and T_3 have direct effects of their own on the pituitary gland, causing an inhibition of the release of TSH.

I know what you're saying: "That's easy for you to say!" But really this control system is not nearly as complex as many in the body.

Now that we have the system outlined, we can begin building our model. Experimentally, T_3 and T_4 were injected into normal animals and we note that it causes blood levels of TSH to decrease. It can be shown that the decrease in TSH level is not as great as would be expected if response was proportional to the amount of T_3 and T_4. Therefore, both a delay proportional feedback and integral feedback from T_3 and T_4 to the pituitary gland was used. The integral feedback term means that the pituitary gland integrates (sums up over time) the amount of T_3 and T_4 in the blood over time. It is not dependent on merely the current level, but also the integral of the level over the last 48 hours. If we ignore the temperature effect on the hypothalamus causing negative feedback, then we can model the level of TSH with Equation 9-6:

$$TSH'(t) = aHT\log[TRF(t)] - b[FT_3(t-48)] - c\int_{t-48}^{t}(FT_3(\tau)-FT_3'(\tau))d\tau - dTSH(t)$$

$$(9\text{-}6)$$

where

$TSH(t)$ = concentration of plasma TSH,

$TRF(t)$ = concentration of plasma TRF,

FT_3 = concentration of unbound T_3 and T_4,

b, c = parameters representing inhibitory effect of T_3 on plasma TSH,

aHT = parameter representing excitatory effect of TRF on TSH release,

d = parameter representing loss rate of TSH in plasma,

FT_3' = normal plasma concentration of unbound T_3 and T_4.

The model presented in Equation 9-6 is based on a model presented in Finkelstein and Carson, *Mathematical Modelling of Dynamic Biological Systems.* This is an excellent, although not elementary, introduction to modelling, and this writer recommends it highly.

When you run a simulation, several output modes are available. You may want a real-time plot of the values computed. When possible (and not too time consuming), this is an informative approach. The plotting routines provided earlier can be used for this. Tables of the data can also be sent to the screen, printer, or disk. Or, if you desire only the result at the end of the simulation, a single number can be printed. In fact, all three can be done at once. You can have a real-time plot on the screen, a table printed on the printer, and the ultimate result sent to a disk file. The world is open to your imagination.

EXAMPLE SIMULATIONS

The chapter wouldn't be complete if we didn't actually set up a couple of models and run them. For the first example, we will consider the removal of a drug from the body. We assume that the removal is proportional to the concentration of the drug in the plasma. The model for this is

$$x'(t) = -ax(t) \qquad (9\text{-}7)$$

The time constant, a, is 2.5. The subject is injected with an amount of the drug necessary to raise its concentration to 100 micromoles per liter. Plot the course of the removal of the drug as a function of time from $t=0$ to $t=20$.

Of course, the constant, a, is chosen rather arbitrarily here, but in a real modelling situation, it can be determined experimentally. Since this is a first-order equation, it can be solved by the Euler, Taylor series, Runge-Kutta, or predictor-corrector methods. See Chart 9-1.

Chart 9-1. Solution to $x'(t) = -2.5x(t)$, $x(0) = 20$

RESULT AT T=	0.10000 IS X=	15.5762
RESULT AT T=	0.20000 IS X=	12.1309
RESULT AT T=	0.30000 IS X=	9.4476
RESULT AT T=	0.40000 IS X=	7.3572
RESULT AT T=	0.50000 IS X=	5.7293
RESULT AT T=	0.60000 IS X=	4.4616
RESULT AT T=	0.70000 IS X=	3.4744
RESULT AT T=	0.80000 IS X=	2.7056
RESULT AT T=	0.90000 IS X=	2.1069
RESULT AT T=	1.00000 IS X=	1.6407
RESULT AT T=	1.10000 IS X=	1.2777
RESULT AT T=	1.20000 IS X=	0.9950
RESULT AT T=	1.30000 IS X=	0.7748
RESULT AT T=	1.40000 IS X=	0.6034
RESULT AT T=	1.50000 IS X=	0.4699
RESULT AT T=	1.60000 IS X=	0.3659
RESULT AT T=	1.70000 IS X=	0.2849
RESULT AT T=	1.80000 IS X=	0.2219
RESULT AT T=	1.90000 IS X=	0.1728
RESULT AT T=	2.00000 IS X=	0.1346
RESULT AT T=	2.10000 IS X=	0.1048
RESULT AT T=	2.20000 IS X=	0.0816
RESULT AT T=	2.30000 IS X=	0.0635
RESULT AT T=	2.40000 IS X=	0.0495
RESULT AT T=	2.50000 IS X=	0.0385
RESULT AT T=	2.60000 IS X=	0.0300
RESULT AT T=	2.70000 IS X=	0.0234
RESULT AT T=	2.80000 IS X=	0.0182
RESULT AT T=	2.90000 IS X=	0.0142
RESULT AT T=	3.00000 IS X=	0.0110
RESULT AT T=	3.10000 IS X=	0.0086
RESULT AT T=	3.20000 IS X=	0.0067
RESULT AT T=	3.30000 IS X=	0.0052
RESULT AT T=	3.40000 IS X=	0.0041
RESULT AT T=	3.50000 IS X=	0.0032
RESULT AT T=	3.60000 IS X=	0.0025
RESULT AT T=	3.70000 IS X=	0.0019
RESULT AT T=	3.80000 IS X=	0.0015
RESULT AT T=	3.90000 IS X=	0.0012
RESULT AT T=	4.00000 IS X=	0.0009
RESULT AT T=	4.10000 IS X=	0.0007
RESULT AT T=	4.20000 IS X=	0.0005

cont. on next page

Chart 9-1-cont.   Solution to $x'(t) = -2.5x(t)$, $x(0) = 20$

RESULT AT T=	4.30000	IS X=	0.0004
RESULT AT T=	4.40000	IS X=	0.0003
RESULT AT T=	4.50000	IS X=	0.0003
RESULT AT T=	4.60000	IS X=	0.0002
RESULT AT T=	4.70000	IS X=	0.0002
RESULT AT T=	4.80000	IS X=	0.0001
RESULT AT T=	4.90000	IS X=	0.0001
RESULT AT T=	5.00000	IS X=	0.0001
RESULT AT T=	5.10000	IS X=	0.0001
RESULT AT T=	5.20000	IS X=	0.0000

For second example, let's observe our forest of wolves and rabbits to see how things go. We can rewrite Equations 1-2 and 9-1 by changing the constants a, b, c, and d so that these equations now have the following form for a predator-prey model:

$$w'(t) = aw(t) - bw(t)r(t)$$

$$r'(t) = cw(t)r(t) - dr(t)$$

(9-8)

with

$$a = 3, \quad b = 0.002, \quad c = 0.0006, \quad \text{and} \quad d = 0.5$$

and initial conditions

$$r(0) = 1000, \quad w(0) = 200$$

This system can be coded in BASIC easily:

```
DEF FN F1(T,X1,X2)=3*X1 - 0.002*X1*X2
DEF FN F2(T,X1,X2)=0.0006*X1*X2 - X2/2
```

The initial conditions are that there are 1000 rabbits to start $(r(t) = 1000))$ and 200 wolves $(w(t) = 200)$. Let's solve the system for $t = 0$ to 10 with a constant step size of $h = 0.2$ and see what happens. Chart 9-2 shows the predator-prey model solution to the system

$$w'(t) = 3w(t) - 0.002w(t)r(t)$$

$$r'(t) = 0.0006w(t)r(t) - r(t)/2$$

with $w(0) = 200$ and $r(0) = 1000$. See Figs. 9-6, 9-7, and 9-8.

If the system is stable, then the wolves and rabbits live in a sort of equilibrium, even though their relative numbers will oscillate. The system just simulated oscillates but it appears to be stable.

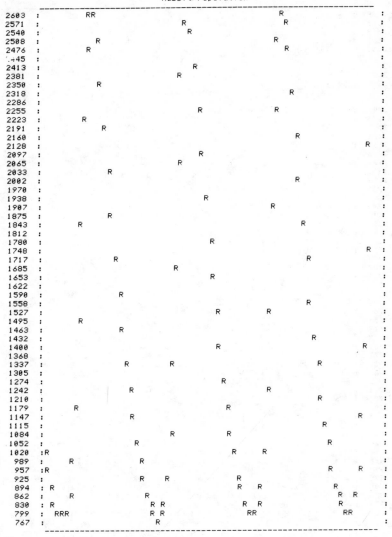

Fig. 9-6. Solution to predator-prey model (rabbits).

Any process that can be described by state and differential equations can be simulated using the methods described in this and the previous chapter. Simulation is an important tool for business forecasting, ecological studies, physiological studies, and for the designing and improvement of many technological advances.

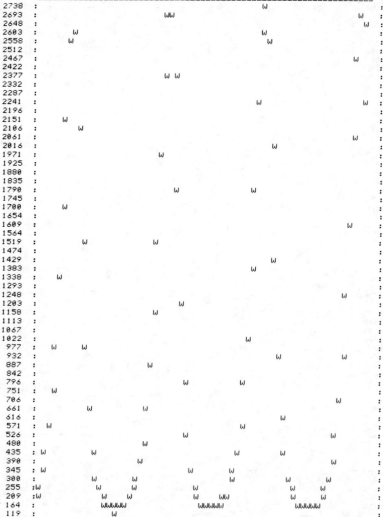

Fig. 9-7. Solution to predator-prey model (wolves).

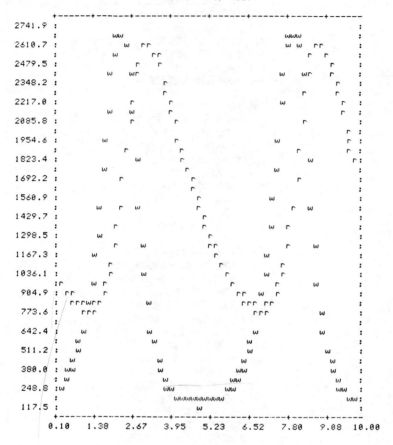

Fig. 9-8. Solution to predator-prey model (wolves and rabbits).

Chart 9-2. Solution to Wolves-Rabbits System

```
        ITERATION STEP 1
X1( 0.200000)= 247.845000
X2( 0.200000)= 929.327000
        ITERATION STEP 2
X1( 0.400000)= 315.257000
X2( 0.400000)= 869.586000
        ITERATION STEP 3
X1( 0.600000)= 409.755000
X2( 0.600000)= 821.557000
        ITERATION STEP 4
X1( 0.800000)= 541.515000
X2( 0.800000)= 786.706000
        ITERATION STEP 5
X1( 1.000000)= 723.492000
X2( 1.000000)= 767.553000
        ITERATION STEP 6
X1( 1.200000)= 970.368000
X2( 1.200000)= 768.302000
        ITERATION STEP 7
X1( 1.400000)=1294.540000
X2( 1.400000)= 795.845000
        ITERATION STEP 8
X1( 1.600000)=1696.020000
X2( 1.600000)= 861.250000
        ITERATION STEP 9
X1( 1.800000)=2142.550000
X2( 1.800000)= 981.330000
        ITERATION STEP 10
X1( 2.000000)=2542.370000
X2( 2.000000)=1177.780000
        ITERATION STEP 11
X1( 2.200000)=2738.200000
X2( 2.200000)=1466.460000
        ITERATION STEP 12
X1( 2.400000)=2586.080000
X2( 2.400000)=1829.610000
        ITERATION STEP 13
X1( 2.600000)=2105.980000
X2( 2.600000)=2195.330000
        ITERATION STEP 14
X1( 2.800000)=1497.430000
X2( 2.800000)=2471.780000
        ITERATION STEP 15
X1( 3.000000)= 974.216000
X2( 3.000000)=2600.560000
        ITERATION STEP 16
X1( 3.200000)= 625.780000
X2( 3.200000)=2586.600000
```

Chart 9-2-cont. Solution to Wolves-Rabbits System

```
                 ITERATION STEP 17
        X1( 3.400000)=  418.187000
        X2( 3.400000)=2483.360000
                 ITERATION STEP 18
        X1( 3.600000)=  292.636000
        X2( 3.600000)=2340.720000
                 ITERATION STEP 19
        X1( 3.800000)=  215.906000
        X2( 3.800000)=2182.700000
                 ITERATION STEP 20
        X1( 4.000000)=  169.560000
        X2( 4.000000)=2020.990000
                 ITERATION STEP 21
        X1( 4.200000)=  141.979000
        X2( 4.200000)=1863.120000
                 ITERATION STEP 22
        X1( 4.400000)=  126.496000
        X2( 4.400000)=1713.170000
                 ITERATION STEP 23
        X1( 4.600000)=  119.472000
        X2( 4.600000)=1573.150000
                 ITERATION STEP 24
        X1( 4.800000)=  119.103000
        X2( 4.800000)=1443.920000
                 ITERATION STEP 25
        X1( 5.000000)=  124.766000
        X2( 5.000000)=1325.710000
                 ITERATION STEP 26
        X1( 5.200000)=  136.728000
        X2( 5.200000)=1218.450000
                 ITERATION STEP 27
        X1( 5.400000)=  156.069000
        X2( 5.400000)=1121.950000
                 ITERATION STEP 28
        X1( 5.600000)=  184.762000
        X2( 5.600000)=1036.050000
                 ITERATION STEP 29
        X1( 5.800000)=  225.899000
        X2( 5.800000)=  960.704000
                 ITERATION STEP 30
        X1( 6.000000)=  284.035000
        X2( 6.000000)=  896.109000
                 ITERATION STEP 31
        X1( 6.200000)=  365.658000
        X2( 6.200000)=  842.834000
                 ITERATION STEP 32
        X1( 6.400000)=  479.702000
        X2( 6.400000)=  802.008000
```

cont. on next page

Chart 9-2-cont.   Solution to Wolves-Rabbits System

```
                ITERATION STEP 33
        X1( 6.600000)=  637.882000
        X2( 6.600000)=  775.635000
                ITERATION STEP 34
        X1( 6.800000)=  854.292000
        X2( 6.800000)=  767.088000
                ITERATION STEP 35
        X1( 7.000000)=1142.970000
        X2( 7.000000)=  781.924000
                ITERATION STEP 36
        X1( 7.200000)=1510.930000
        X2( 7.200000)=  829.153000
                ITERATION STEP 37
        X1( 7.400000)=1942.980000
        X2( 7.400000)=  922.878000
                ITERATION STEP 38
        X1( 7.600000)=2376.610000
        X2( 7.600000)=1083.000000
                ITERATION STEP 39
        X1( 7.800000)=2680.900000
        X2( 7.800000)=1330.080000
                ITERATION STEP 40
        X1( 8.000000)=2690.560000
        X2( 8.000000)=1664.970000
                ITERATION STEP 41
        X1( 8.200000)=2339.360000
        X2( 8.200000)=2039.210000
                ITERATION STEP 42
        X1( 8.400000)=1760.890000
        X2( 8.400000)=2363.120000
                ITERATION STEP 43
        X1( 8.600000)=1183.350000
        X2( 8.600000)=2559.130000
                ITERATION STEP 44
        X1( 8.800000)=  758.666000
        X2( 8.800000)=2602.960000
                ITERATION STEP 45
        X1( 9.000000)=  497.641000
        X2( 9.000000)=2532.020000
                ITERATION STEP 46
        X1( 9.200000)=  341.667000
        X2( 9.200000)=2402.990000
                ITERATION STEP 47
        X1( 9.400000)=  246.196000
        X2( 9.400000)=2250.460000
                ITERATION STEP 48
        X1( 9.600000)=  188.191000
        X2( 9.600000)=2089.710000
```

Chart 9-2-cont. Solution to Wolves-Rabbits System

```
                    ITERATION STEP 49
        X1( 9.800000)=  153.347000
        X2) 9.800000)=1929.890000
                    ITERATION STEP 50
        X1(10.000000)=  133.088000
        X2(10.000000)=1776.480000
                    ITERATION STEP 51
        X1(10.200000)=  122.643000
        X2(10.200000)=1632.250000
                    ITERATION STEP 52
        X1(10.400000)=  119.509000
        X2(10.400000)=1498.490000
                    ITERATION STEP 53
        X1(10.600000)=  122.599000
        X2(10.600000)=1375.680000
                    ITERATION STEP 54
        X1(10.800000)=  131.815000
        X2(10.800000)=1263.840000
                    ITERATION STEP 55
        X1(11.000000)=  147.887000
        X2(11.000000)=1162.850000
                    ITERATION STEP 56
        X1(11.200000)=  172.390000
        X2(11.200000)=1072.500000
                    ITERATION STEP 57
        X1(11.400000)=  207.906000
        X2(11.400000)=  992.712000
                    ITERATION STEP 58
        X1(11.600000)=  258.321000
        X2(11.600000)=  923.564000
                    ITERATION STEP 59
        X1(11.800000)=  329.238000
        X2(11.800000)=  865.453000
                    ITERATION STEP 60
        X1(12.000000)=  428.483000
        X2(12.000000)=  819.249000
                    ITERATION STEP 61
        X1(12.200000)=  566.553000
        X2(12.200000)=  786.546000
                    ITERATION STEP 62
        X1(12.400000)=  756.605000
        X2(12.400000)=  770.069000
                    ITERATION STEP 63
        X1(12.600000)=1013.080000
        X2(12.600000)=  774.333000
                    ITERATION STEP 64
        X1(12.800000)=1347.050000
        X2(12.800000)=  806.706000
```

cont. on next page

Chart 9-2-cont. Solution to Wolves-Rabbits System

ITERATION STEP 65
X1(13.000000)=1754.910000
X2(13.000000)= 878.923000
ITERATION STEP 66
X1(13.200000)=2197.360000
X2(13.200000)=1008.470000
ITERATION STEP 67
X1(13.400000)=2573.220000
X2(13.400000)=1216.790000
ITERATION STEP 68
X1(13.600000)=2722.230000
X2(13.600000)=1516.400000
ITERATION STEP 69
X1(13.800000)=2518.230000
X2(13.800000)=1881.980000
ITERATION STEP 70
X1(14.000000)=2011.430000
X2(14.000000)=2236.490000
ITERATION STEP 71
X1(14.200000)=1411.080000
X2(14.200000)=2491.500000
ITERATION STEP 72
X1(14.400000)= 915.471000
X2(14.400000)=2597.350000
ITERATION STEP 73
X1(14.600000)= 592.218000
X2(14.600000)=2567.890000
ITERATION STEP 74
X1(14.800000)= 399.329000
X2(14.800000)=2458.030000
ITERATION STEP 75
X1(15.00000)= 281.973000
X2(15.00000)=2313.420000
ITERATION STEP 76
X1(15.200000)= 210.242000
X2(15.200000)=2155.280000
ITERATION STEP 77
X1(15.400000)= 166.903000
X2(15.400000)=1994.640000
ITERATION STEP 78
X1(15.600000)= 141.202000
X2(15.600000)=1838.440000
ITERATION STEP 79
X1(15.800000)= 127.011000
X2(15.800000)=1690.450000
ITERATION STEP 80
X1(16.000000)= 121.009000
X2(16.000000)=1552.480000

Chart 9-2-cont.   Solution to Wolves-Rabbits System

```
                   ITERATION STEP 81
            X1(16.200000)=  121.588000
            X2(16.200000)=1425.290000
                   ITERATION STEP 82
            X1(16.400000)=  128.272000
            X2(16.400000)=1309.070000
                   ITERATION STEP 83
            X1(16.600000)=  141.454000
            X2(16.600000)=1203.750000
                   ITERATION STEP 84
            X1(16.800000)=  162.354000
            X2(16.800000)=1109.140000
                   ITERATION STEP 85
            X1(17.000000)=  193.118000
            X2(17.000000)=1025.110000
                   ITERATION STEP 86
            X1(17.200000)=  237.061000
            X2(17.200000)= 951.666000
                   ITERATION STEP 87
            X1(17.400000)=  299.030000
            X2(17.400000)= 889.063000
                   ITERATION STEP 88
            X1(17.600000)=  385.884000
            X2(17.600000)= 837.963000
                   ITERATION STEP 89
            X1(17.800000)=  506.977000
            X2(17.800000)= 799.634000
                   ITERATION STEP 90
            X1(18.000000)=  674.398000
            X2(18.000000)= 776.290000
                   ITERATION STEP 91
            X1(18.200000)=  902.293000
            X2(18.200000)= 771.628000
                   ITERATION STEP 92
            X1(18.400000)=1203.810000
            X2(18.400000)= 791.712000
                   ITERATION STEP 93
            X1(18.600000)=1582.940000
            X2(18.600000)= 846.302000
                   ITERATION STEP 94
            X1(18.800000)=2017.700000
            X2(18.800000)= 950.432000
                   ITERATION STEP 95
            X1(19.000000)=2434.400000
            X2(19.000000)=1124.490000
                   ITERATION STEP 96
            X1(19.200000)=2692.460000
            X2(19.200000)=1386.970000
```

cont. on next page

Chart 9-2-cont.   Solution to Wolves-Rabbits System

```
              ITERATION STEP 97
        X1(19.400000)=2635.680000
        X2(19.400000)=1731.340000
              ITERATION STEP 98
        X1(19.600000)=2233.080000
        X2(19.600000)=2099.770000
              ITERATION STEP 99
        X1(19.800000)=1645.440000
        X2(19.800000)=2402.050000
             ITERATION STEP 100
        X1(20.000000)=1094.050000
        X2(20.000000)=2569.030000
```

BASIC CONVERSIONS

If you have a computer other than a TRS-80 disk system, then probably at least some of the programs presented in this book will require some translation before they will run on your computer. The programs should work with virtually all versions of Microsoft BASIC, with the exception of the screen graphics routines. To facilitate the translation of the programs, we will discuss some of the special features of Microsoft BASIC and alternative ways to program them. These include DEF FN, INSTR, and PRINT USING. The other functions used, such as LEFT$, RIGHT$, and MID$, have direct analogs in the most popular BASICs, including Atari and Applesoft BASIC. The approach may be different from Microsoft, but the translation is a single statement. Consider B$=LEFT$(A$,2), which returns a character string containing the two leftmost characters in A$. This function is supported by Applesoft BASIC. Atari BASIC would simply use an assignment statement, B$=A$(1,2). Since Atari BASIC does not support string arrays, some of the programs that plot on a line printer must be substantially changed. A suggested approach is to dimension a single string long enough to hold the "string array," and use pointers to positions within the string to maintain artificial boundaries for the "array elements." It is difficult to be all things to all people, especially in computer programming.

The DEF FN feature of Microsoft BASIC is a powerful one, but not indispensable. It can be replaced with a subroutine. It is important to note that user-defined functions (noted by preceding their names with "FN") allow local variables in passing parameters. For example, if you have the function FN MAX to return the larger of two values:

```
DEF FN MAX(A,B) = -(A>B)*A - (B=>A)*B
```

Then you may use any variables (or constants) when referencing the function. You may invoke it with

```
Z = FN MAX(X,Y)
```

In this case the X is substituted in for A in the function's definition, and the Y is substituted in for the B. The variable names do not have to coincide. When you write a subroutine in BASIC, you do not have this luxury—they must coincide. Consider a subroutine that does the same thing as FN MAX:

```
1000 IF A>B THEN Z=A
1010 IF B=>A THEN Z=B
1020 RETURN
```

The subroutine must have the two values in variables A and B—no other variables will be accepted. To call it, you must make sure that the parameters are passed correctly. The calling routine below sets up the parameters and calls the routine:

```
200 A=X:B=Y
210 GOSUB 1000
220 AN=Z
```

Since we want the larger of X and Y, we must put them into variables A and B. This sets up the parameters as the subroutine expects them. The GOSUB calls the routine at line 1000. The result is returned in variable Z, and this is passed into variable AN by the calling routine. This emulates the single statement AN=FN MAX(X,Y).

In some of the programs we used a selector function. One of the parameters was used to choose from among a group of functions. For example, consider the system:

```
10 DEF FN SEL(S,A,B) = −(S=1)*FN MIN(A,B) − (S=2)*FN MAX(A,B)
20 DEF FN MIN(A,B)= −(A<B)*A−(B<=A)*B
30 DEF FN MAX(A,B)= −(B<A)*A−(A<=B*B
```

If the parameter passed in variable S is 1, then the FN MIN is chosen, and parameters A and B are passed to it. If S=2, then FN MAX is chosen. This is a tricky programming technique, but quite useful when you have a number of functions to evaluate. This can be redone in subroutine form as well:

```
2000 IF S=1 THEN GOTO 2030
2010 IF S=2 THEN GOTO 2070
2030 PRINT"ERROR":RETURN
2040 REM MINIMUM
2050 IF A>B THEN Z=B ELSE Z=A
2060 RETURN
```

```
2070 REM MAXIMUM
2080 IF A>B THEN Z=A ELSE Z=B
2090 RETURN
```

The logic of the program and the logic of the selector function are the same. The implementation is the only difference. Again, the parameters must be set up properly. To emulate AN=FN SEL(K,X,Y), you must use the following routine:

```
300 S=K:A=X:B=Y
310 GOSUB 2000
320 AN=Z
```

Because subroutines use global variables, you must be very careful that your subroutine does not alter the value of any important variables inadvertently. Consider the following example:

```
20 FOR I=1 TO 10
30   GOSUB 1000
40 NEXT I
50 END
1000 I=I-1
1010 PRINT I
1020 RETURN
```

This will result in an infinite loop printing out "0" endlessly. But the result in the following user-defined function is a loop that prints out 1 through 10:

```
10 DEF FN F(I)=I-1
20 FOR I=1 TO 10
30   PRINT FN F(I)
40 NEXT I
```

The point is that when you use subroutines you must be careful not to alter the values of variables inadvertently. This kind of error can be quite elusive to track down during debugging, particularly in complex programs using nested subroutines. One technique to avoid this is to use variables with the second letter of the variable denoting the level of the nesting of the subroutine. Thus "A" would be an outer variable, "A1" one subroutine level, "A2" one deeper, etc. Procedure-oriented languages, such as PL/1 and Pascal avoid this problem completely, and the BASICs that support DEF FN go part way to eliminating this kind of error. When you translate the user-defined subroutines in this book, watch specifically for altering variables inadvertently.

Another useful feature of Microsoft BASIC is INSTR(S$,A$,P), which returns the starting position of A$ within S$, beginning the search at character position P in S$, where S$ is the string to be searched, and A$ is the string to be searched for. If P is omitted, then the search begins with the first character in S$; if specified, then it begins at position P in S$. If a match is found, then the character position within S$ that matches A$ is returned; if not, then a zero is returned. For example,

INSTR("This is a string","a s")

returns a "9," because that is where A$ occurs in S$. Since some BASICs lack this feature, here is a subroutine that performs this function:

```
1000 REM subroutine to replace INSTR in Atari BASIC
1010 REM global variables are:
1020 REM    HZ$ = source string
1030 REM    PZ$ =substring to be found
1040 REM    JZ = starting position for search
1050 REM    KZ = holds returned value
1060 KZ=0
1070 FOR IZ=JZ TO (LEN(HZ$)-LEN(PZ$)+1)
1080    IF LEN(PZ$)>LEN(HZ$(IZ)) THEN IZ=1000:GOTO 1100
1090    IF HZ$(IZ,IZ+(LEN(PZ$)-1))=PZ$ THEN KZ=IZ:IZ=1000
1100 NEXT IZ
1110 RETURN
```

A somewhat more difficult task is to emulate the powerful PRINT USING formatting statement of Microsoft BASIC. We will only concern ourselves with formatting numbers in the form ####.####. The # character stands for a digit position. This function is very useful for formatting output into nice readable columns. If there are not enough digits to the left of the decimal point to fill it out, then the field is padded with blanks. If there are not enough digits to the right of the decimal point, the field is padded with zeros. Both Applesoft and Atari BASICs lack this feature. The routine below performs it by first turning the number into two strings (the integer part and the fractional part) and then processes the string by padding the left portion with blanks as necessary, and padding the right side with zeros or truncating the fractional portion, whichever is appropriate.

```
1000 REM       PRINT USING Subroutine in Applesoft BASIC
1010 REM       PASSED PARAMETERS
1020 REM          NL=# OF DIGITS TO THE LEFT OF DECIMAL PT
1030 REM          NR=# OF DIGITS TO THE RIGHT OF DECIMAL PT
1040 REM          AZ=VARIABLE HOLDING VALUE TO BE PRINTED
1050 REM       PRINTS OUT FORMATTED NUMBER AS S$
1060 AI=INT(AZ):AF=AZ-AI
```

```
1070 SL$=STR$(AI)
1080 SL=LEN(SL$)
1090 LL=NL-SL
1100 IF LL<=0 THEN 1140
1110 FOR IZ=1 TO LL
1120    SL$=" "+SL$
1130 NEXT IZ
1140 IF AF=0 THEN SR$="."
            ELSE
                  SR$=RIGHT$(STR$(AF),LEN(STR$(AF))-1)
1150 SR=LEN(SR$)
1160 LR=NR-SR+1
1170 IF LR<=0 THEN 1210
1180 FOR IZ=1 TO LR
1190 SR$=SR$+"0"
1200 NEXT IZ:GOTO 1230
1210 IF LR=0 THEN 1230
1220 SR$=LEFT$(SR$,NR+1)
1230 S$=SL$+SR$
1240 PRINT S$;
1250 RETURN
```

These three routines are the most specialized features used in this book. Although conversion to your particular BASIC may not have been discussed, it should be made easier now by this exploration of expanding these features as subroutines. Since the subroutines are written in BASIC, they will be slow, but they should work well if you provide a little thought into your translation.

ANALYTICAL FORMULAS

This appendix contains the basic and commonly used formulas of algebra, geometry, trigonometry, and calculus.

ALGEBRA

$A^x A^y = A^{x+y}$
$(A^x)^y = A^{xy}$
$A^{-x} = 1/A^x$
$\log_a x = \log_b x \times \log_a b$
$\log_a x^n = n \times \log_a x$

GEOMETRY

Area of a circle $= \pi r^2$
Circumference of a circle $= 2\pi r$
Area of a rectangle $=$ base $\times$ height
Area of a triangle $=$ (base $\times$ height)/2

TRIGONOMETRY

$\sin^2 x + \cos^2 x = 1$
$\tan x = \sin x/\cos x$
$\cos x = \sin (\pi/2 - x)$
$\sin x = \cos (\pi/2 - x)$
$\cos x = \cos (-x)$

$\sin x = -\sin(-x)$

$1 + \tan^2 x = \sec^2 x$

$\sin(\alpha + \beta) = \sin \alpha \cos \beta + \cos \alpha \sin \beta$

$\sin(\alpha - \beta) = \sin \alpha \cos \beta - \cos \alpha \sin \beta$

$\cos(\alpha + \beta) = \cos \alpha \cos \beta - \sin \alpha \sin \beta$

$\cos(\alpha - \beta) = \cos \alpha \cos \beta + \sin \alpha \sin \beta$

$\tan(\alpha + \beta) = (\tan \alpha + \tan \beta) / (1 - \tan \alpha \tan \beta)$

$e^{ix} = \cos x + i \sin x$ $\qquad\qquad i = \sqrt{-1}$

$\sin x = (e^{ix} - e^{-ix})/2i$

$\cos x = (e^{ix} + e^{-ix})/2$

$\sin \alpha + \sin \beta = 2 \sin((\alpha + \beta)/2) \cos((\alpha - \beta)/2)$

$\cos \alpha + \cos \beta = 2 \cos((\alpha + \beta)/2) \cos(\alpha - \beta)/2)$

DIFFERENTIAL CALCULUS

In the following formulas, a is a constant, f and g are functions, e the base of the natural logarithms, and x is the independent variable.

$(f + g)' = f' + g'$

$(fg)' = fg' + f'g$

$(f/g)' = (gf' - fg')/g^2$

$f(g)' = (f'(g))g'$

Examples

$$d(\sin(\cos x)/dx = \cos(\cos x)(-\sin x)$$

$$= -\sin x \, \cos(\cos x)$$

f(x)	f'(x)
a	0
x	1
x^a	ax^{a+1}
e^{ax}	ae^{ax}
ln x	$1/x$
sin x	cos x
cos x	$-\sin x$
tan x	$\sec^2 x$
sec x	sec x tan x
$\log_a x$	$(\log_a e)/x$
arcsin x	$1/\sqrt{1-x^2}$
arccos x	$-1/\sqrt{1-x^2}$
arctan x	$1/(1+x^2)$

INTEGRAL CALCULUS

In the following formulas, f, g, u, v, and y are functions of x only, n is an integer, e is the base of the natural logarithms, a and b are constants, and F is a function of a function of x. The constants of integration are not written but implied.

$\int adx = ax$

$\int af(x)dx = a \int f(x)dx$

$\int g(y)dx = \int g(y)(dy/dx)dx$

$\int udv = u \int dv - \int vdu = uv - \int vdu$

$\int x^n dx = x^{n+1}/(n+1)$

$\int e^{ax}dx = (1/a)e^{ax}$

$\int (1/x) \, dx = \ln x$

$\int b^{ax}dx = (1/(a \ln b))b^{ax}$ $\hspace{2cm} (b>0, \, b \neq 1)$

$\int \ln x \, dx = x \log x - x$

$\int a^x \ln a \, dx = a^2$ $\hspace{3.5cm} (a>0)$

$\int dx/(a^2 + x^2) = (1/a) \arctan (x/a)$

$\int dx/\sqrt{a^2 - x^2} = \arcsin (x/a)$

$\int \sin x \, dx = - \cos x$

$\int \cos x \, dx = \sin x$

$\int \tan x \, dx = \ln (\sec x)$

$\int (a + bx)^n \, dx = (a + bx)^{n+1}/b(n+1)$ $\hspace{1.5cm} (n \neq -1)$

$\int \sin^2 x \, dx = (x/2) - (1/4) \sin 2x$

$\int \cos^2 x \, dx = (x/2) + (1/4) \sin 2x$

$\int F'(g(x)) \, g'(x) \, dx = F(g(x))$

Example

$$\int [d(\sin(\cos x))/dx][d(\cos x)/dx]dx = \int [d(\sin(\cos x))/dx](- \sin x)dx$$

$$= \cos(\cos x) + C$$

REFERENCES

Abramowitz, M. and Stegun, I.A.
Handbook of Mathematical Functions, Dover Publications, New York, New York, 1972.

Burden, P.L., Faires, J.D., and Reynolds, A.C.
Numerical Analysis, Prindle, Weber, and Schmidt Publishers, Boston, Massachusetts, 1978.

Carson, B. and Goldstein, M.
Rational Approximation of Functions, Los Alamos Scientific Laboratory LA-1943, Los Alamos, New Mexico, 1955.

Cheney, W. and Kincaid, D.
Numerical Mathematics and Computing, Brooks/Cole Publishing, Belmont, California, 1980.

Finkelstein, L. and Carson, E.R.
Mathematical Modeling of Dynamic Biological Systems, John Wiley & Sons, Inc., New York, New York, 1979.

Hamming, R.W.
"Stable Predictor-Corrector Methods for Ordinary Differential Equations," *Journal of ACM,* Volume 6, pages 37–47, 1959.

Harris, L.D.
Numerical Methods Using FORTRAN, Charles E. Merrill Books, Columbus, Ohio, 1964.

Hastings, C.
Approximations for Digital Computers, Princeton University Press, Princeton, New Jersey, 1955.

Isaacson, E. and Keller, H.B.
The Analysis of Numerical Methods, John Wiley and Sons, New York, New York, 1966.

Johnson, L.W. and Riess, R.D.
  Numerical Analysis, Addison-Wesley Publishing, Reading, Massachusetts, 1977.
Krogh, F.T.
  "Algorithms for Changing the Step Size," *SIAM Journal of Numerical Analysis,* Vol. 10, No. 5, pages 949–965, October, 1973.
Maron, M.J.
  Applied Numerical Analysis, Macmillian Publishing Company, New York, New York, 1982.
Miller, A.R.
  Basic Programs for Scientists and Engineers, Sybex Books, Berkeley, Caifornia, 1981.
Randall, J.E.
  The Use of Microcomputers for Physiological Simulation, Addison-Wesley Publishing, Reading, Massachusetts, 1980.
Ruckdeschel, F.R.
  Basic Scientific Subroutines, 2 vols., McGraw-Hill Books, New York, New York, 1981.
Stiefel, E.L.
  Introduction to Numerical Mathematics, Academic Press, New York, New York, 1963.
Weeg, G.P. and Reed, G.B.
  Introduction to Numerical Analysis, Blaisdell Publishing Company, Waltham, Massachusetts, 1966.

Index

C

D

E